To be a Gypsum Miner

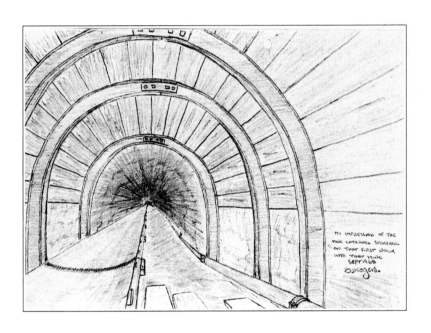

MY IMPRESSION OF THE
MINE ENTRANCE STAIRWELL
AND THAT FIRST WALK
INTO THAT MINE
SEPT 1968
BJRogers.

To be a Gypsum Miner

C. R. Rogers

The Pentland Press
Edinburgh – Cambridge – Durham

First published in 1994 by
The Pentland Press Ltd
1 Hutton Close
South Church
Bishop Auckland
Durham

ISBN 1-85821-189-1

Typeset by Carnegie Publishing, 18 Maynard St., Preston
Printed and bound by Antony Rowe Ltd., Chippenham

I dedicate this book to my wife Irena

for the support and infinite patience she has shown to me throughout our thirty-nine years of marriage. In all of those years she has had to go along with my weekends away potholing, caving, parachuting, and years of exploring old mine workings. All of these pursuits most wives would not have tolerated but she never once complained. For this I must thank her most sincerely.

Contents

Introduction   ix

Stamphill Mine

The first shift   1
Settling in   8
Belt move   10
Tractor man   13
Barring down and charging   14

Jobs in the Mine

Birks Mine   20
First go at drilling   23
Firing a drift   29
Old workings and cavities   32
Crystals   35
Chaside rig   39
Roof bolting   42
Floor shots   45
Shot firing, full time   46
Back to Well Drift   50
Roofing back in Wells   51
Pate Hole Cave   53
Bunker job   54
Mine rescue team   58
Stamphill Cave-in   65
The accident   69
Drifts below the railway   72
Our pets   73
The lower level   82
Newbiggin Mine   94

Stamphill Mine Well Drift 1968–69   125
Birks Head Mine 1969–71   125
Longriggs Mine 1972–87   126
Newbiggin Mine 1987–93   127

Introduction

The author of this book, Carl R. Rogers, was born in Kettering in Northamptonshire in 1935, left school at fifteen, and joined the Army in 1953 at the age of seventeen and a half. After training as a tank driver at Catterick in North Yorkshire, he was posted to the tank firing ranges at Warcop in Westmorland in May 1953. He married while serving in the Army in 1955. On his demob from the Army in 1956, he returned to his native town of Kettering where he took up employment in one of the local shoe factories. At this time there were a number of the local shoe factories closing down with many of the shoe workers being made redundant, future prospects in the shoe trade did not look good. While spending a short holiday with his wife's parents at Warcop, he was offered a job by the MOD working on the firing ranges with the Signals Works Services who maintained the telephone systems on the ranges, where he had already spent his military service. He accepted the offer and returned to Warcop with his wife. He was to spend the next eight years working for the MOD on the firing ranges. During the time he worked there he became very interested in the geology of the area, and in particular the old lead and barytes mines that dotted the fells and were long since abandoned. He had visited some of these mines before during his Army service, in the company of two very good friends, and had at that time become very interested in rocks, and had collected one or two pieces of the many different minerals to be found in the area. The old Dowscar Mine at the head of Scordale Valley had been one of his favourite places to visit, the spoil heaps at that time, having been almost untouched, had been full of fine specimens of fluorite, galena, and quartz crystal. Dowscar Mine had been but one of the many of the Hilton and Murton Mines he had looked into with his two Army friends.

In those days the mines had been reasonably safe to enter, but over the many years he would spend exploring them, they rapidly began to deteriorate, becoming highly dangerous to enter, and since blown in by the military. The two Army friends had also introduced him to the delights of camping on a zero budget, rock climbing the hard way, and potholing, never dreaming that in the years ahead he would be doing such things on a regular basis, combining a hobby and pleasure at the same time.

After some eight years working on the ranges at Warcop, and feeling the need for a change of employment, with perhaps better prospects, he applied for and was accepted as an AA patrolman, to work the A66 road with another good friend. The two of them worked the road between Penrith and Bowes on the Yorkshire side, as it was then. The author would spend his first winter as an AA patrolman riding a motorcycle with sidecar across the bleak moors of both Stainmore and Bowes Moor when required to cover the other patrolman's days off. After spending five very happy years as a patrolman with the AA, and by this time having three children and a mortgage to keep up with, he decided very reluctantly to seek a job that paid a little more in wages, to keep up with the ever increasing cost of living. He was informed by a friend that two men were wanted to work in the Stamphill Mine at Kirkby Thore. He decided to go to the mine and try his luck.

Stamphill Mine

The first shift

I arrived at the Stamphill Mine at about noon on the Saturday morning. It's a good thing my pal had explained to me how to find the mine or I would not have found it. I parked my car and walked over to the office, knocked on the door and waited. A voice said 'Come in.' It was Mr Parkin. I had never met him before and he appeared to me to be a very quiet spoken man. I said to him, 'I am looking for a job.' He looked up at me with his big soft eyes and said, 'Where are you from, lad?' 'Warcop,' I replied. 'Ah yes I know Warcop,' he said. 'What kind of work have you been on with?' I told him I had been an AA man for over four years, on the road between Penrith and Bowes. 'Right you can start tomorrow on night shift, is that all right for you?' 'Yes,' I heard myself saying a bit surprised. 'Thanks very much, I will be here tomorrow at ten o'clock sharp.' And that was that.

I walked over to my car wondering what had I let myself in for and drove home. 'I start on the night shift tomorrow,' I told my wife. I don't know who was more surprised, my wife of myself. I suddenly realised I had not discussed wages or conditions nor anything else for that matter, I suppose in a way that's how things were done in those days.

I arrived at the mine as the men were clocking on. I joined them and when I arrived at the clock found a card already there for me with my name on and a number; I put my card through the clock. A tall man came to me and told me to go to the lamp house, this was George the foreman. He sorted a lamp out for me from one of the many lamps on the lamp rack, he also gave me a new leather belt and a new helmet. He put the battery on my belt and the lamp onto my new helmet. 'These are yours, look after them, remember the number on the lamp, that is your lamp now, don't ever take someone else's.' By this time the other lads had collected their lamps and taken off down the mine; just the one big lad remained behind, the big lad Edwin, who had been instructed by George to keep an eye on me and see

1

I came to no harm. I would be working with Edwin on the vibrator, and for the next few shifts I would stick to Edwin like glue, that is until I understood the basics, how to find my way to and from the bait cabin, to and from my places of work in the mine. Edwin would keep his eye on me in general until it would be safe enough to let me walk about the mine on my own. 'Have you got your bait bag with you?' It was Edwin, 'Yes,' I replied. 'Right then, let's be going, we are running late.' We stepped into the mine entrance alongside of the main belt with Edwin in the lead, myself following, we were heading for the bait cabin down the mine. The very first thing I noticed as we entered the mine was the smell, like moist clay, a kind of dampness, just a little like being in a cave. But after a short while I didn't notice it any more. We walked beside the main haulage belt, it was quite low, we had to bend to avoid hitting our heads in some places, and rough walking at times. At one point we passed some steel girders arched over the drift and filled in with lagging boards. I noticed the roof here looked wet and grotty.

We carried on until the tunnel began to widen out a little and we could stand more upright. I noticed other tunnels, or rather drifts, as we walked on following the belt, just some of the old workings, water in some of them I could see. All at once we began to descend quite a steep gradient, about one in eight, at this point the drift widened out and became much higher. It surprised me, I had not expected it to be as big as this at all. I had also been surprised by the lighting in this drift, from what Edwin had called the tandem or transfer point at the top of the hill. The whole drift being lit up, we walked to the bottom of the incline, and stopped here to cross the main belt while it was stationary, on the other side of the belt we turned a sharp corner to our left. What a sight met my eyes: there in front of me and all lit up with the lights on the side of the drift, the belt running away in front of me as far as I could see away down the hill, the Well Drift. I shall never forget that first time I looked down that drift, it seemed to me to go on forever. I had stopped, and had to hurry to catch up with Edwin. We had to bend to go under a couple of cross belts coming onto the main belt, and went on and on for what seemed ages.

Eventually we arrived at the bait cabin. Two of the lads were having their tea. 'Put your bait bag down somewhere for now and we can have a cup of tea before we start.' I looked around me, a plank or two set on breeze blocks to sit on and old lagging boards to rest your back on. A huge electric motor sat in the middle of the cabin, mounted on a set of bogey wheels, and, just to keep the place tidy, an empty powder box to throw our waste in. By the time I made my tea with hot water, from an urn outside the cabin, the other two lads had gone. 'I will pick you up on the way past. Wait here for me, I won't be too long,' said Edwin, and he was gone. I was now alone. It was very quiet. I could hear a soft rumbling noise and stepped outside to see what it was, it was only the main belt running.

After what seemed like ages I heard the sound of a vehicle coming down the back drift, I opened the door to that drift and stepped out. Coming down the drift I saw Edwin driving a Hough 30 front end loader. He told me to climb up onto the tractor and hold on tight, and off we went, downhill at first and at the bottom, a sharp right hand turn that took us right under the main belt. After we had travelled for quite some distance, we arrived at the place in the workings where we would be loading. Edwin showed me where to connect the jackhammer up to the airline, the on/off switch for the vibrator, I knew what the big hammer was for. I sat on the lagging board there for that purpose and waited for the first load. I did not have long to wait, Edwin raised the bucket on approach to the vibrator and tipped carefully, the rock dropped into the vibrator with a crash, I switched it on and rock began to feed out of the hopper onto the belt. We were in business. Edwin tipped the rest of the load and shot off to get another, I batted the big lumps with the hammer to break them up, it took a while to empty the vibrator, and Edwin came back with a load before the first had all been emptied out of the vibrator. I had a fair share of rough stuff in those first few loads, and had quite a bit of spillage to shovel up in between loads. The dust had not been enough to bother me at all, and only the odd really big lump to stick in the vibrator that I had to use the jackhammer on. 'Bait time,' Edwin shouted.

So this was my first shift. I climbed up on the tractor and we set off for the bait cabin; I would really try to remember the way this time. By the time we arrived back at the bait cabin I was totally lost, I just could not understand how, in such a short distance as we had travelled, I could become so confused. To me all the roads in the place looked the same, no wonder I was so confused. I climbed down from the tractor, and entered the cabin, put a spoon of tea into my pot, and stepped outside to the tea urn. Each

3

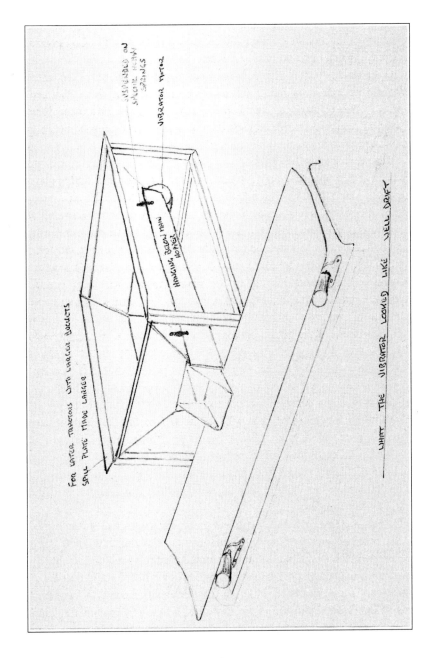

SUSPENDED ON SPECIAL HEAVY SPRINGS

VIBRATOR MOTOR

HANGING BELOW MAIN HOPPER

FOR LATER TRACTORS WITH LARGER BUCKETS SPILL PLATE MADE LARGER

WHAT THE VIBRATOR LOOKED LIKE   WELL DRIFT

cabin had an urn for boiling the water for the men's tea. Stepping back into the cabin, as I was the last man in, I shut the cabin door and looked around, each man had his own place to sit, except me.

Edwin told me where I could sit, without getting a good bulling as he put it. I was lucky, my place was in a corner, from now on in this cabin, with these lads on this shift, this would be my place. I sat down on the short plank set up on concrete blocks, and put my aching back against the lagging board there for that purpose, set my tea down amidst the dust, and opened my bait box.

I was suddenly aware of eight pairs of eyes watching me. 'Where dost thou cuffray then?' I heard a voice boom out. It was Geordie, the big lad sat on the other side of the cabin, one of the drillers, I didn't know this at the time though. 'Warcop,' I replied. That seemed to satisfy everyone's interest for the time being at least. Inside the cabin there was a telephone, if that's what you could call it, one of the old wind up type. George the foreman did his rounds on this, at bait time, checking with men in other parts of the mine to see all was well, to keep them informed, or to request information from them.

I also noticed while I sat there eating, what appeared to be a metal tube

THE FIRST BAIT CABIN I SAT IN   WELL DRIFT   SEPT 1968

set up on the side of the drift, on special brackets, and when I enquired about this I was told it contained a stretcher, and other items of first aid in case of accident.

This was something I had not even considered until now. I sat quietly and listened to the lads chatting away to each other about this and that, nothing in particular, I was beginning to feel more comfortable already.

'Are you lot going to do any work tonight? Come on then, let's be having you.' It was George the foreman, the half hour bait time had passed so fast, I hadn't noticed it. The lads rinsed their pots and were away, I rinsed my pot and put it with my bait box. 'Make sure the lid is on your bait box.' It was Edwin, 'And put it away in your bag,' he said, 'or the mice will go with your bait.'

Mice, how could mice get down here? Just having me on I thought, but he wasn't, as I would shortly find out. By this time we were outside, back on the tractor bumping along the road, back to where we were loading rock from. I climbed over the belt when we arrived there, took up my position by the vibrator, and was ready for action again.

I had a few moments before Edwin would be back with a load of rock for me so I looked around me for the first time. My God, what a height the roof was, it must have been all of twenty feet or more, this surprised me but the vastness of the place we were in was awesome to say the least.

I had just not taken a good look around me until now—what a place we were in, like standing in a cathedral and looking up at the roof, the way the roof had been arched over. They had been fired like this, I had been told by Edwin, to stand the enormous pressures on them; much safer than a flat roof he had told me, in this type of rock. The reason they were so high being, when first fired, they had only been about twelve feet high, then the floor had been fired out twice; if not the floor, then the roof would be fired out. Just then George arrived to see me again, just checking to make sure I was okay. I had quite a lot of spillage on the floor by this time, and he stopped to give me a hand to clear it up, for which I was grateful. He had a quick word with Edwin and then he went off up the belt, I watched as his light disappeared into the distance, it seemed a long way off before it finally passed from sight. I heard the buzz and jingle of a machine going in the distance, only a rock drill could make a noise like that, I thought to myself. I listened to the clatter of the jackhammer, as I began to break up yet another of those big ones that had jammed the mouth of the vibrator. As I listened to it, I imagined just for a moment what it must like to be a driller, and just then the jackhammer slipped off the rock I was breaking and took some skin off the back of my hand. I had already taken skin off my shin, not to mention the lump of rock that rolled onto my foot off the belt, on the very first load. I did not have steel toecaps in my boots at this time, but I knew one thing, the next pair I bought would have. I brought the hammer down hard, to strike yet another lump of oversize rock that had just dropped onto the belt.

As the hammer struck home a piece of rock flew up striking me on the side of the face, I wondered if this happened to others doing the same job, or if it was just not my night. Edwin stopped the tractor every now and again to ask if I was coping. He just smiled when I showed him my bleeding hand. 'Thou will soon learn,' he said. It was time for our second bait and I felt ready for mine by now, it was early morning, the first night shift I had put in since my army days.

I climbed up on the tractor and off we went for our second bait of the shift. This time I had a much better idea where I was going, I could actually remember some of the route and this pleased me very much. It didn't seem to take as long this time, but then it never does if you have some idea where you are going, and in this place that took a bit of time to sink in, every road looked exactly the same to me. We arrived back at the cabin a little later than the other lads, brewed our tea and sat down to eat what was left of our sandwiches.

For the first time I had a really good look around at the lads in the bait cabin. What a state they were in. It was easy enough now to see who the drillers were, covered in grey or white, gypsum dust. They sat there with their helmets off, their hair wet with perspiration, faces covered thick with the dust. We had no washing facility down here, just a cold tap to rinse your hands, or you could put your handkerchief under the tap on the urn, for hot water. I looked down at myself and as mucky as I had become by this time I was nothing like these lads. As I looked at the faces around me I tried hard to remember the names; only one could I bring to mind, that was Geordie, the one who had asked where I came from, apart from Edwin, and George the foreman. At this time in the morning we were feeling really tired, I could have shut my eyes and fallen

7

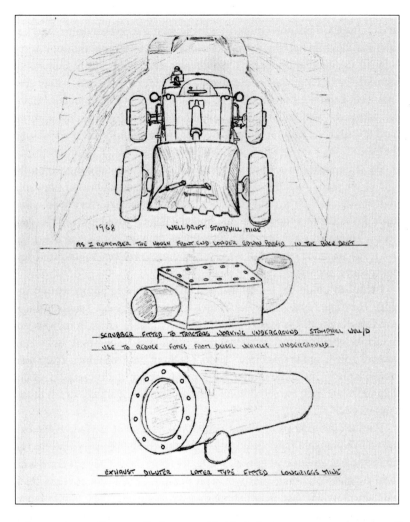

1968 WELL DRIFT STANHILL MINE
AS I REMEMBER THE HOUGH FRONT END LOADER EDWIN PARKED IN THE BACK DRIFT

SCRUBBER FITTED TO TRACTORS WORKING UNDERGROUND STANHILL WELL/D
USE TO REDUCE FUMES FROM DEISEL VEHICLES UNDERGROUND

EXHAUST DILUTER LATER TYPE FITTED LONGRIGGS MINE

asleep quite easily, very little was said this bait time, we were by now all too tired to want to be bothered.

'Are you lot going to do any work?' a voice boomed out, it was George. 'Come on then, let's be having you.' We all got up to wash our pint pots out, as if stunned into action. I rinsed my pot and put it in my bait bag, outside the cabin I climbed on the tractor again and we set off back to the old number one district, and our vibrator. 'I only have about a half a drift to lead out, and it will be time to knock off,' I heard Edwin say as I cleaned up at the vibrator. I switched the belt on and sat back on a lagging board and waited for the first load to be tipped in, and so it went on: tractor up to the vibrator, tip to vibrator, I switch vibrator on, rock comes through onto belt, I break the big lumps, belt takes rock away up the belt. I didn't know where the rock went to at that time. Actually it took it away up the drift through a chute and dropped it onto the main belt which took it all the way to the top of the hill, and tipped it into the underground bunker. I would find these things out later after I had been in the mine a little longer. 'That's the last,' Edwin shouted to me as he tipped in. 'Turn the air off and take the jackhammer off. I will give you a hand to clean up around the vibrator.' After we had done that I put the shovel and the jackhammer in the bucket along with the big hammer, and we were on our way. He dropped me off at the bait cabin. 'Wait there till the rest of the lads come in and come up with them, I will see you when you come up the drift.'

I picked up my bait bag and stepped through the cabin door. It must be some length of belt, I thought, as I looked down the drift it seemed to me to stretch for miles. All at once there was a sharp crack, immediately followed by a muffled thump. I could feel a vibration in the air around me, in the far distance, away down the belt a light appeared, bobbing towards us. 'That's it, they are firing, come on lad we had better be going now,' one of the two lads standing with me outside the cabin said, and with that they stepped up onto the belt and were gone. I knew then I would not be stepping onto that belt. I set off to walk up the drift. I could see a light away in the distance, shining back towards me, it was Edwin, waiting for me.

The pale yellow glow of the lights up the side of the drift, seemed to put a shine on the empty belt as I walked, I listened to the jingle of the rollers, as the belt joints passed over them. 'Didn't get lost then?' It was Edwin. 'Come on then we had better get a move on lad.' I saw a couple of lads in front of us, they seemed to appear from nowhere. 'Where did those lads come from?' I enquired. 'That's the fitter and electrician, their cabin is just through that brattice. If we have time tomorrow night I will show you around the workshops, before we start work.' I stopped at the corner and turned to have a look back down the drift—what a sight, looking back down the hill toward the main heading, the lights on the side of the drift disappearing into the distance.

We turned the corner, there were two lads standing on a wooden staging, waiting to step onto the belt, this belt moving a lot faster than the one we had just walked alongside. Edwin told me this was the main belt for outside, and it was faster than the others. If I had any doubt at all about riding it, I should walk around the bottom of the belt, as some of the older men preferred to do. I thought, in that case I will have a go, I will want to ride it some time or another, in the future. As the lads in front of me stepped onto the belt, I took notice how they leaned forward as they stepped on to keep balance. Edwin turned to me and said, 'When you step on the belt, just go down on your hands and knees and stay there till you reach the top of the hill, I will be behind you in case you slip.' I stepped onto the belt, bent my knees, leaned forward and was on my way; I had no difficulty in standing, and rode the belt to the top of the hill, stepped off on the staging but had to grab the handrail as I stepped off. There were a number of men standing at the transfer point, this being a place where the rock dropped from one belt onto another, it was known by the lads as the tandem. It is normally a very dusty place to be when rock is going through it, I could feel the cold morning air on my face as I stood there waiting my turn to ride the belt. I watched as one by one they threw themselves face down, flat out, and took off on the belt, the last leg on the way to the surface. At this point I turned and began to walk alongside the belt, I just could not bring myself to get on that belt, flat out, as the others had done. I was surprised how far it was to walk out of the mine from the tandem, but at least it gave me a chance to have a look around as I walked. I could see now why the lads had to lay flat out on the belt, the roof was lower than I had thought, and there were two very low points in the roof, just before I reached the girders I had seen on the way down at the start of the shift. I could see long abandoned workings to my right in the light of my cap lamp, some water in there reflected the light from my lamp onto the roof. It made a fine pattern on the roof when I threw a small piece of rock into the water, it sounded to be quite deep, by the plop it made. The air smelled fresh and sweet as I reached the mine entrance. Good thing I had decided to walk, I thought, as I reached the point where the lads would have had to jump off the belt—I would have broken my neck.

'That cap lamp has a number on it, make sure it goes back in its proper place on the rack.' It was Edwin again. 'Well, what did you think if it then?' he said to me. 'Oh all right,' I heard myself saying, I wasn't really sure though. I felt a little like a freak, the way I was stared at while waiting to clock off, but then, don't all the new blokes get stared at wherever they may be? I was tired, all I wanted to do was get home and into bed.

Settling in

The next few weeks would be very much of the some kind of thing. I could find my way to the bait cabin okay, after the first shift, and I soon became accustomed to loading points in the mine, depending on where the rock had been fired. I also became an old hand at riding the belts. I met a lot of the miners and they found out all they wished to know about me. Some of the lads remembered me from seeing me on the road as an AA patrolman, I was surprised by this, but it pleased me. About this time, during the occasional slack periods we would have while loading, due to belts stopping or whatever, I would take the opportunity to take a look around the place. I had heard and seen machines in the distance but could not see what they were doing. Edwin told me he would have to give the road a good clean up, to clear the spillage so I would have a few minutes to spare; I could hear the noise of a hand machine going, and set off to see it. I saw only a cloud of dust in the distance, and by this time I had to get back to the loading point. Oh well another time, I thought to myself as I switched the vibrator on.

In time I got to know the lads quite well, they had a great sense of humour and loved a bit of fun, it certainly helped to make life in the mine more tolerable. One thing surprised me though, the way they took pity on the mice in the bait cabin, from that very first bait time when the mice had come out, and the lads had thrown little bits of cake to them. When I asked how they came to be so far down the mine, I was informed they would have followed the belts down. I thought it more probable that although they did enter this way at first, as the workings were driven deeper and deeper, so the offspring of those first mice ever to enter the mine and their offspring would follow the miners, and their bait cabins.

During one shift we had a bit of time to spare, this was my opportunity to see what Ken the driller was doing in a drift quite close to where we were loading rocks. I followed the dust trail into the drift, I could see nothing at all for the dust, as I got in a little closer to the terrific noise the machine was making, I could just see the dull glow of Ken's cap lamp, and the outline of him standing there, holding the machine in a fog of dust. What surprised me the most was that he had his pipe in his mouth. He looked across at me very briefly and carried on drilling. By this time I was choking with the dust anyhow, and I turned and walked back out of the drift, pleased to be able to breathe again. I had not quite expected this, and it had come somewhat as a surprise to me—shock would be more honest—it took the glamour off the drilling job straight away, for the time being at least. Back at the vibrator I sat, thinking of Ken drilling, not quite as I had imagined it to be, the dust just for starters, and the noise of that machine, bad enough standing two drifts away, never mind standing and holding it. I walked back to the vibrator and stood waiting for Edwin to bring another load of rock, I could hear a machine coming, it seemed to take ages before it came into sight, and what a sight! It looked huge from where I stood. I had no idea at the time but this was the Hudson Scaling Carriage. I had heard it mentioned on many occasions, but this was the first time I had seen it. This machine had a Ford tractor at the rear of it, two wheels at the front operated by two hydraulic rams, making it articulated. The boom could be raised by means of an hydraulic ram, either by the driver on the tractor, or by one of the two men it could take in the cage. It could also traverse to left or right by using the steering rams, operated by a small lever mounted in the driver's compartment, the same lever that the driver would use to steer the vehicle, there being no steering wheel fitted. In all a very useful machine to have around the mine. It would be used for roof bolting mainly, but also for many other jobs besides.

I did get a chance to have a good look at it, later in the week. The first thing I noticed was the stoper standing in the cage of the machine, it was designed for drilling holes in the roof, not drifts. Simple really to look at, the actual rock drill being mounted in the vertical position, on top of the air leg, all in one piece. The rock drill used by Ken had the air leg separate from the actual machine, but was bolted to it, allowing the man using it to put horizontal holes into the face, and also to reach up to put holes high in the face and roof or floor.

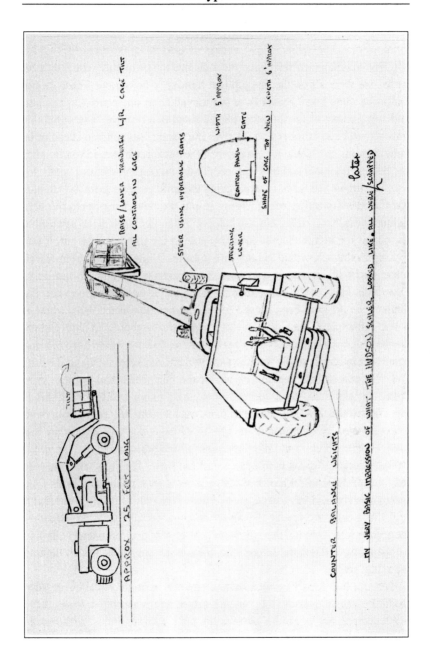

RAISE / LOWER TRAVERSE L/R CAGE TILT

ALL CONTROLS IN CAGE

STEER USING HYDRAULIC RAMS

STEERING LEVEL

WIDTH 5' APPROX

CONTROL PANEL

GATE

SHAPE OF CAGE TOP VIEW LENGTH 6' APPROX

TILT

APPROX 25 FEET LONG

COUNTER BALANCE WEIGHTS

MY VERY BASIC IMPRESSION OF WHAT THE HUDSON SCALER LOOKED LIKE, ALL ONES SCRAPPED

later

13

Belt move

My first maintenance shift gave me a chance to get to know the lads a bit better, we were all on the one job that Sunday, a belt move. These moves had to be done fairly regularly as we moved from one district to another, and I might say of all the jobs going I liked a belt move. The move this time would be in number five district. The tractor had gone on ahead of us with the tools and tackle for the move in the bucket, we arrived shortly after the tractor, the tools and tackle tipped by the side of the vibrator, ready for use. The driver had made a start digging the spillage away from the vibrator already, the first thing we did being to put the belt clamps onto the belt, tighten these down tight, then the pullifts. When tightened up these enabled us to split the belt at the belt joint, by pulling the jointing wire out; if this was tight, the belt would be cut with a knife. While this had been taking place, some of the lads would have been carrying the pans to put on to extend the belt. At the same time, as soon as the belt had been split, the vibrator would have been moved to its new position in the drift, where it would remain until the next move. It would now be about bait time, and we would walk back to the cabin for our bait. After bait we would have to bring some breeze blocks to the job, the pans would be spaced out along the drift and then placed into position on top of the belt which had by now been pulled out along the floor, starting where the vibrator had first been standing. We would have to look the pans over before we could bolt them together, some of them had quite a bit of damage, due to the fact they had been well used before in the mine. Some of the pans had to be hammered straight along the sides before we could use them. If rollers were missing they would have to be replaced, there were always plenty of spares. The return idlers would have to be pushed under the belt as it lay on the floor, then lifted onto two breeze blocks set on edge, the pan sides would sit on the return idler, two of the lads would have a bag of nuts and bolts and would start putting these through the holes in the pan sides, to bolt them to the return idlers.

When a few pans had been bolted together, a single metal cover plate would be placed over the joint at each return idler and bolted down. If the holes did not line up in the sides of the pans with the holes in the return idler, then the shout would go out for the podger. This useful tool had been made by grinding one of the hardened steel bolts that once held a rock drill together, the fitters made these for us and I don't think we could ever have put some of the bolts in without one. When all the pans had been put in and bolted together, usually about seven on a belt move at that time, the belt would have had its ends cut square by the fitter and new joining combs put on to them. The new length of belt would be joined to the old piece, the belt could now be pushed through the belt end roller, a heavy steel roller inside a steel box. A short hole had been bored into the floor at the back of the box, a roof bolt would be pushed down this hole, and a length of steel cable attached, held on by means of a steel plate on the end of the roof bolt, this would hold the box down when the belt was running. After the belt had been pulled through the box, it would be joined up after being tightened with the pull lift. The vibrator would be moved into position on the end of the belt using the tractor. By this time, the electricians would have moved the cables and switches for the vibrator and have reconnected them. While this work was taking place, two lads would have brought in some more airline pipe. The pipes would be joined onto the existing airline pipes, which at this time were laid on the floor and not hung from hooks in the roof. Before the taps could be put on the end of the pipes, the main stop tap, which had been turned off at the start of the job could now be turned halfway on to blow any dust and small chippings out of the new pipes.

When all had been completed the belt would be run to check it out, see it ran true, the vibrator checked, and that would be that.

All this work took time to complete in a shift, but the lads knew just what to do and just got on with it, they did not have to be told. I did notice each man seemed to have a job he favoured on these moves, and after a while I found I had mine also.

As time passed I would settle down to mining like a duck takes to water, mainly because I found it so interesting; every day there would be something new to be learned, those first few weeks would make a lasting impression on me, that was for sure. I had by this time made my mind up, I would be a driller shotfirer, that's what I had my sights on, and that's what I would be.

During those first weeks in mining I was hardly able to take in the sheer size of the underground workings. I had no idea there were such vast caverns beneath the fields of Kirkby Thore, almost a potholer's dream come

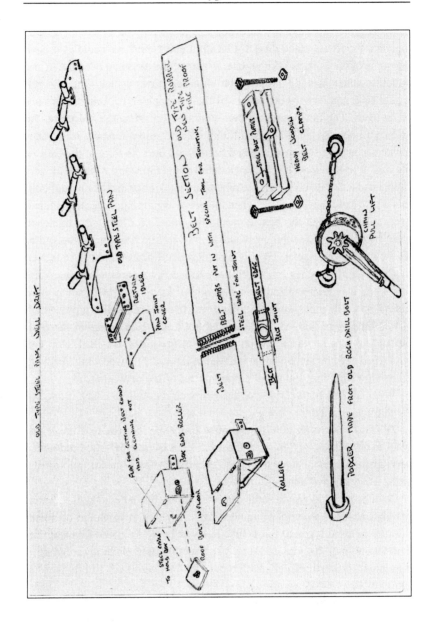

true. The roadways in the mine would be about sixteen feet wide on average, the height of roof varied from one place to another, from as little as eight feet to as high as twenty-six feet or more where an area had been floored out. At this time the Well Drift to me was the mine, I did not realise that this was but one part of the mine and there were many more parts I had not seen or heard of. I did not know what a brattice had been built for, but did know what a brattice was. I had no idea what an air door was put in for, this for the time being would be my little world, and I would learn and find out for myself a little about mining during the time I would spend working here in Well Drift. I was, as the lads would say, 'gey thick about mining,' but would soon learn. For the time being at least, my tools would be a jackhammer, shovel and big hammer.

In the weeks to follow I would become familiar with the names of the different districts in the Well Drift, the number one and two districts, number five district, Well Drift west, and the main heading, to name just some. The main heading was reputed to be all of a thousand feet deep at its furthest point, to me this sounded interesting. I had not yet been that far down, although I had often stood looking back down the main belt, to where it disappeared into the blackness, beyond the last light in the drift.

Tractor man

After I had worked at the mine for six weeks Edwin asked to come off loading with the tractor. I couldn't believe my luck when I was asked if I would learn to load, and go onto the tractor as the loader. I accepted there and then, keen to learn one of the more responsible jobs in the mine, and slightly better bonus that went with the job. Again Edwin had to take me in hand and teach me how to operate the controls for the bucket on the vehicle, and the vehicle itself. The driving controls were simple enough, but driving into a heap of rock and coming out again with a bucket full of rock was something else, as I soon found out. I soon had the job in hand, having been shown how, and would learn a lot the hard way in the following weeks. I would soon be loading as skilfully as the other loaders, and doing my best to keep the rock going up that belt, that rock paid our bonus, and I had no intention of letting the other lads down on this point.

I had been loading for about three months when the foreman asked me to go into the main heading to load some rock out, at that time the main heading had been stopped because of poor quality rock. Geordie had been put in there to split the double pillars as we pulled back out of the heading, the rock fired, I would load out onto the main belt through a vibrator set on the end of the belt. As the pillars were split and loaded out we had to move the vibrator back up the hill, and shorten the belt at the same time. The lads were already saying the Well Drift had almost been worked out, and would not be mined for much longer. Those lads who had been in this situation before, at the Cocklakes Mine near Carlisle, when it had closed and they had come to Stamphill Mine to work, were noticeably more concerned than we were. I began to have doubts myself as to my future in mining at this time, and began to consider very carefully the alternatives open to me. In the meanwhile all any of us could do was get on with the job in hand and hope that something would work out in the end that might be helpful to us all.

Barring down and charging

When Edwin had been instructing me on the tractor, one of the first things he had done had been to take me into a drift that had been barred down and ready for loading out. This was to show me the difference in one that was safe to load out, and one that was not safe to load out. He then took me to one that had been in the process of being barred down. It was most important I should know the difference, because I could get seriously injured if I did not. He took me to a drift that Ken had already made a start on. I was taken by surprise by the size of some of the pieces of rock that had already been barred off by Ken, and could see now why Edwin had been at pains to get into my head at the time the dangers of loading a drift out that had not been barred down. I stood well outside of the drift as Ken worked carefully, keeping very close into the side, using a long steel bar made from an old drill steel. Some of the slabs came off easily, others not so easy and he had to use a lot of strength on the bar to get these to come off. He would give the roof a good bat with the end of the bar, now and then, and from where I stood I could hear the difference in the sound it made as he struck the roof. There would be a good sound ring to it if the roof was good and hard, but only a dull thud if it were not.

When he had finished the roof, he took a pick and hacked off any loose rock he found on the face and sides of the drift, it could now be loaded out.

'This drift is finished if you want it,' Ken said as he came out of the drift. He took his bar and the pick and put them to one side, in a cut out of the way, and went off to start drilling. After he had gone, I just had to pick the bar up and feel the weight of it, what a weight! I had no idea they were as heavy as this, it was a good seven feet long, with a sharp chisel end, bent at about forty-five degrees. It was no wonder Ken had taken his helmet off, to wipe the perspiration from his face when he had finished barring down, I had seen steam rising from his head, and his hair had been wet. 'How do you fancy that for a job then?' It was Edwin. 'I am not too sure,' I said. He just laughed. I had taken note though, and I would make sure I never loaded a drift out unless it had first been barred down.

I had settled down to being a loader by this time, and with the hassle of getting the tonnage that went with the job, we were still very busy, and did not have too much time to spare during a shift. During one night shift the bunkers became full, I had a little time to wait before I could continue with the loading, so I took this opportunity to walk around to where I had heard Ken drilling. By the time I had walked around to his drift he was busy charging, I stopped, but he said it was all right for me to go in, this being something I had wanted to see, charging in progress. We talked for a few minutes, me asking questions, he answering them. I watched, fascinated, while Ken used a tool made of brass, called a prodder, to make a hole in the pill or stick of powder. After he had done this, he took a detonator from the leather det box he had with him and pushed it into the hole he had made in the end of the pill. After this he took hold of the wires coming out of the end of the det, made two loops in it, pushed these over the pill of powder and pulled them tight. The pill was then inserted into the shot hole. Holding the loops of det wire in one hand, the pill with the det in was pushed down the hole using the stemming stick, seven more sticks of powder followed this down the hole, and one clay cock. The powder used at that time came in four-ounce waxed cartridges, and the shotfirer would use his own discretion as to how much powder he used per hole. On average I would think it

19

would be seven sticks plus the primer with the det in, which worked out about two pounds of powder per hole. Some might use a lot less, and fire a drift with many more large pieces of rock in, the man on the vibrator would spend more time breaking these up, the belts would be stopped wasting valuable loading time.

The clay cock I mentioned was no more than some clay that had been picked up on the way down to the bait cabin at the start of the shift, if you knew where to look, and rolled out to use as stemming. The stemming normally used at that time was squares of brown paper rolled up on the stemming stick to form a tube, and filled with dust from the holes. This of course would be pushed down the hole last, and tamped up using the stemming stick.

By this time the belts had started up again and I had to get back to my loading. It had been the first time I had ever been near to any of the explosive used in the mine, in fact it was the first time I had seen the stuff. It had been very interesting to see charging taking place, and I would not stop thinking about it for the rest of the shift.

It was at the end of this particular shift that I did something very silly, and would be reminded of it many times after the event by those lads who had witnessed it.

We stood outside the clock office waiting to clock off, at around five fifty p.m. I had done some bragging about my climbing ability, I looked up at the high storage bin where the rock from the mine would be tipped above the outside crusher. 'I could climb that no bother,' I said. 'Bet you couldn't,' one of the lads replied. Before I realised what I was about, I climbed up the drainpipe on the building next to the bin, about thirty feet, run along the rigging of the roof, and climbed up to about forty odd feet off the ground. I had climbed up the outside of the bin using the nuts and bolts sticking through the steel sheets that made up the sides, until I had reached some brickwork, only this had stopped me reaching the top. During the climb I heard shouts of encouragement from the lads below watching, one voice seemed louder than the rest, in fact much louder, repeating over and over, 'Come down, you silly bugger!' It had started to rain just a little, as I made my way down amid the cheers of the lads. It was time to clock off. As I put my card through the clock, and stepped out of the door, I was grabbed by a very angry Herbert, the man in charge at that time. 'Don't you ever do anything like that again,' he said to me, 'or you will go down the road. I don't mind if you want to kill yourself but don't do it in company time and on company property.' Thankfully that was the last I heard of it from him, but it would be the talk of the mine for some time to come.

Jobs in the Mine

I had by this time asked to have my name put down for a drilling job should one become available, I was assured my name would be put on the list. I liked the job I had driving the shovel loader, it being one of those jobs that kept me busy; it also allowed me to keep in touch with the drilling side. I had had plenty of practice checking the drifts to see if they had been barred down, and I sometimes had time enough to spare to watch some charging being done, and sometimes drilling. In the Well Drift the jobs, as far as I could tell, were very well organised, the drilling done with hand machines, the drillers barred the drifts down, charged their drifts, fired them at the end of shift, they also stood in on the outside aerial job if required. They would roof bolt when asked, go belt cleaning, and go on the scraper at the back of the bunker and scrape back, if necessary. As loaders we did all the loading, sometimes we would be asked to do some belt cleaning, we would do this too at times when the main belts had stopped to assist the man on the vibrator, to keep the belts from the vibrator clear, and also help him if we had a lot of big lumps to load out of a drift, after they had been tipped into the vibrator. It sometimes happened an oversize lump of rock would block one of the chutes, taking the rock to the main belt from the vibrator. When this happened, the belt would trip itself out on power and stop. If the chute blocked, and the belt did not trip out, we sometimes had a huge pile-up of rock at the chute, this would have to be cleared up, and often an electrician would have to be called out to restore power.

The man on the vibrator would be there to watch for oversize rock coming through the vibrator, and break them down before allowing them to travel up the belt, due to the number of chutes the rock would sometimes have to pass through on its way to the underground bunker. He would keep the belts clear of spillage from the vibrator, and make sure he left the place tidy at the end of his shift, and report any damage, splits in the belt or whatever. The men were expected to muck in on maintenance shift to do

22

anything that had to be done, although at that time a local builder had a contract to build the brattices in the mine.

In the Well Drift we had the Hudson scaling carriage, this being used for roof bolting, and sometimes for firing bad roofing out before bolting took place. Situated at the bunker bottom, by the main control room for the mine's belts system, an underground laboratory had been built, this being used for quality control, samples of rock dust from all the working faces in the mines would be brought in for testing. By testing the dust, the percentage of gypsum would be known in each of the drifts where samples had been taken from, if the quality became poor, the drift would have to be stopped, as had happened in the main heading.

The man who worked in the control room would be responsible for starting all the belts up at the beginning of the shift, he would watch the main control panel during his shift, this panel had a plan of all the main belts in the two mines, with different coloured lights. The belts could, in emergency, be switched off by anyone at any time by means of a pull key simply operated by pulling hard on a cable attached to the belt structure, and running the length of that belt. The man in the control room would also set the vibrators used to feed rock from the bunker onto the belt taking it to the surface. At times he would operate the scraper on the stockpile at the back of the bunkers. A belt cleaner had a section of belt that he would be responsible for, he would have to make sure it was kept clear of any spillage,

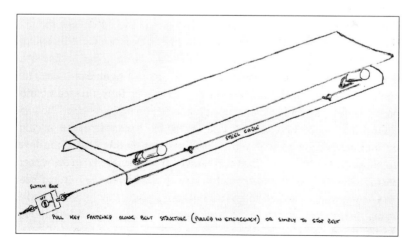

PULL KEY FASTENED ALONG BELT STRUCTURE (PULLED IN EMERGENCY) OR SIMPLY TO STOP BELT

if a blockage occurred he would sort it out. He might be required to cover more than just one section of belt, any large pieces of rock falling from the belt would have to be cleared, any faults found or damage to the belts or rollers would have to be reported.

Both the fitter and electrician on shift would be on call whilst on shift, if they were not called out during the shift they would be expected to do other maintenance work, or carry on with whatever repairs had not been completed by the previous shift. At the time I worked at Stamphill a blacksmith employed at the mine had a workshop on the surface, and did some amazing work at times, he made all the bars for use in barring down, sharpened drills and performed many other jobs that came within his skills.

I had by this time had the opportunity to get to know the lads doing the roof bolting in the Well Drift, I had been asked by them to clear a pile of roofing they had fired, to enable them to get in to roof bolt. After I had done this for them I carried on loading. I could hear their machine going while I loaded out in the drift next to theirs; during a short belt stoppage period I walked around to see what they were doing. They had stopped to allow the dust to get away, the cage was lowered to have a crack with me and they explained how the roof bolts had to be put in. They took turn about, one man on the tractor seat one shift, and change about the next, all the scaling would be shared between them, it made the job easier if only one man was in the cage, doing the actual bolting. I was allowed to hold the machine and work the controls, the machine, or stoper as it was referred to, being a rock drill mounted vertically on an airleg all in one piece. To change the drill steels, the retaining bar was pulled back from the collar on the drill, and the drill simply lifted out, a new one put in and the locking bar pushed back over the collar. I turned the hand control on the right hand side, this controlled the air leg, the machine lifted, I raised it up fully, pressed a button on the same control and the machine dropped down again, I turned the hand control fully off and it remained still. On the left hand side of the machine the air control lever being down in the closed position, as I eased this lever up, the drill steel began to rotate very slowly. If I had pushed it to the vertical position the drill would rotate on full power with percussion. It had been very interesting, but I had to get back to my loading now. I had hoped to watch them putting a bolt in, oh well another time perhaps. I had no idea that, in the years to come, I would do all of these jobs.

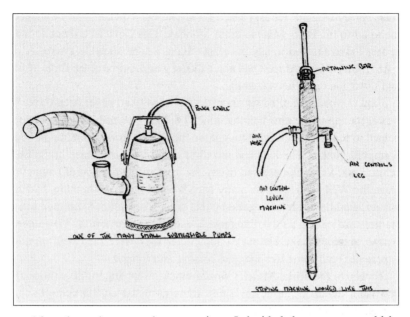

After about three months as a miner, I decided three years would be enough for me, hopefully by then I would have paid a bit off my mortgage, and might find some other employment. I suppose really it was natural for me to think this way, the number of men coming to the mines and also leaving them, although I might add some of those who left did return at a later date. It seemed to me at that time there would always be something new to learn about mining, and at the time changes were already beginning to take place, in all three mines. I didn't mind the shifts, but I did miss seeing the children as often as I would have liked to.

Birks Mine

After some three months of working in the Well Drift, I had settled down to mining very well. I still knew little about it as yet but thought I did. I was happy enough at this time and enjoyed my work as a loader and in fact had become quite expert at it. I think most people do if they are contented in their work. Then came the day the man in charge of the mine at that time,

John, came to see me. He asked how I was getting on then told me he wanted me to go to the Birks Mine as from Monday. This came as a shock to me, in fact I was stunned to say the least. 'Have I done something wrong?' I asked him. He assured me I had not, a loader was required at the Birks Mine and I was the one who was going.

I knew where the mine was situated but as yet had never been there. It was at the top of the nine belt that much I did know, I had on one occasion helped to repair the belt that brought the rock down from that mine into the Stamphill bunker. The lads had talked of the mine many times in the bait cabin. I was very disappointed to say the least, at the thought of having to leave the Well Drift, and the many friends I had made down there, having become familiar with the routine by this time. I had noticed that men were starting and leaving all the time though, and as one man left the job another would come and take his place. Sometimes they were men with mining experience, and some like me, just coming into mining.

To get to the Birks Mine, I would clock on at Stamphill as normal, and walk down the mine the same route as usual until I came to the bunker bottom, from there instead of turning left for the Well Drift, I would have to turn right, where the main control room was situated, and through to the bottom of the nine belt. From there I looked up the hill to where I would now be working; the hill I had to walk up was in fact a cross cut that had been blasted through to link up Birks Mine with Stamphill Mine, it had been completed a short while before I had started at the mines. This cross cut had been driven through some bad ground, much of it through sandstone; it was very wet and muddy, it would be about one in eight, and something like seven hundred yards in length. The main belt, or nine belt as it was known, came down on one side of the drift, with a haulage way on the other side of it. We would walk up the hill between the metals, stepping on the boards the metals were fastened to. The drift was lit up all the way to the top of the hill, the walk to the top really was rough, water everywhere, just mud and puddle all the way up. I noticed as I walked up the hill, metal sheets had been placed over the belt in many places, to keep the water off as it dripped through the roof; if the rock on its way from Birks to the bunker in Stamphill had become too wet, it would set solid in the bunker at the Stamphill end. It had been a fair hike up to the top of the hill and when

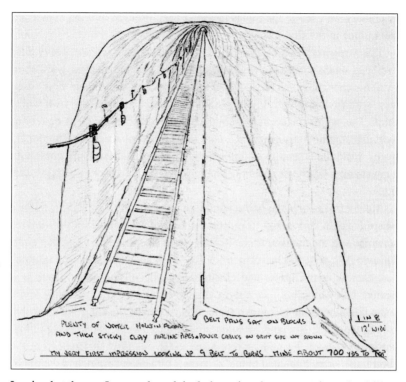

PLENTY OF WATER HOLES IN FLOOR
AND THICK STICKY CLAY AIRLINE PIPES & POWER CABLES ON DRIFT SIDE NOT SHOWN
BELT PANS SAT ON BLOCKS
1 IN 8
12' WIDE
MY VERY FIRST IMPRESSION LOOKING UP 9 BELT TO BURNS MINE ABOUT 700 YDS TO TOP

I arrived at the top I remembered the lads saying that, at one time, the drillers had carried their powder for the shift, packed in special canisters, plus det box up the hill. I was thankful that all I had carried on this occasion had been my bait bag. I stood and looked back down the hill, and wondered what I had let myself in for this time.

I called in at the fitting shop at the top of the hill as was the practice, to have a crack with the lads I would now be working with; I was quite impressed with their workshops. They had been well planned out and were well equipped. They could do almost anything in the way of repairs to the vehicles and machinery used in the mines from the rock drills in use, the drill rig they had in this mine and the tractors used for loading. The electricians had their work cut out also, in the maintenance of all the electrical equipment in use, including static plant, pumps, all the vehicles used for loading, transformers. It had always amazed me how all this equipment and machinery we used in the mines had ever been brought into the mine from the surface in the first place.

The workshops had well made pits for vehicle maintenance, heavy duty overhead block and tackle, welding gear, both gas and electric, good solid work benches, in which the lads had their own drawers for their tools. They were well fitted out with lighting, and the electricians had their own workshop. The whole place had a solid concrete floor to make it better for working on which also made it easier to keep the place clean. The miners would wind the fitters up at times by saying, if a man was any good with a hot spanner (burners) and a big hammer, he was half way to being a mine fitter.

My foreman at Birks Mine would be Johnnie. He came in to tell me where I would be loading from, and the lad who would be on the vibrator soon showed me the way to the loading point we would be using that shift. This would not be too far away from the fitting shop, so we would take our bait time with the fitters and electricians at the fitting shop. There was another bait cabin, but this was located at the other end of the mine, quite some distance from where we were now, the main heading being in that part of the mine. It would be some time before I would be working in that particular area of the mine. Birks Mine itself was little different from the Well Drift, or so it seemed to me; perhaps a bit less in height, and the roads, at least where I worked at this time, would be more level. The work would be done much the same as in the Well Drift, the drifts were drilled with hand machines, and after firing and dressing down I would load the rock out into a vibrator, from there it travelled via the belt system to the Stamphill bunker.

I should point out things were very much different from this at the other end of the mine, in the main heading, but I was not aware of this at the time, and any drilling I had seen taking place had all been done with hand machines only. I would soon become friendly with the two young lads who were doing the drilling in this area of the mine, in fact these two lads would teach me to drill with a hand machine later on. Life for me in the mine at this time was great, I really enjoyed my job as a loader, and as I became more familiar with the mine the more I liked it. Every day seemed different for me, always something new to learn or find out, it really was a very exciting period in my life. I looked forward to coming to work, and not many could say that these days. Even now when I look back over that period in my life, it still gives me a great deal of pleasure; the work was hard, and could be very monotonous, but the lads took it in their stride and were always cheerful, they did not have to be told what to do, we each had our job to do and got on with it. During the course of a shift there would be little time to spare, rock had to go up that belt to make our pay, the higher the tonnage, the higher the bonus.

In this part of the mine where I now worked, there were the two lads doing the drilling, the vibrator man, and myself. As a loader I would do my very best to load out all the rock the drillers had fired; if they had only fired one drift each on the shift, I could quite easily catch up with them, and they knew this. To keep ahead of me, and have more rock in the drifts than I could load out in the shift, they would fire an extra drift each every other day. To do it they would have to have a good start at the beginning of the shift, get one drift bored and charged before second bait. They would then set to after bait and bore half a drift on for the next day. When they came in on the next shift, they would bore the other half of the drift started on the previous shift, then bore another drift, and get both drifts charged before the end of the shift. It may sound easy enough to do, but anyone who thinks it easy, I suggest they should try it, after first dressing a drift down at the start of the shift. Having charged two drifts each, and fired them, they would have four drifts to bar down between them on the next shift when they came in. If there was one thing a driller hated most it was to have the loader breathing down his neck, and if there was one thing a loader liked most, it was to be breathing down the neck of a driller. But there was no ill feeling just a bit of friendly rivalry.

First go at drilling

I was shortly to have my first taste of drilling, and it came about very simply; one of the drillers, Nipper, wanted to have a go at loading. We came to an agreement, he would teach me to drill, I would teach him to load, towards the end of the shift we would have almost completed our work, but I would make sure to have some rock left to load, Nipper would then finish off the loading of this rock. In the meantime Nipper would have left his machine set up in the drift, and mark where the holes had to be placed. I had already been shown how the machine operated. Having left him to load I took hold of the drill, it almost put me on my back, this was an Atlas machine, slightly heavier than a Silver Three, and with a longer air leg on than a Silver Three.

I struggled just to hold the thing up. 'Come on, lad,' I said to myself, 'shape up.' I lifted the seven-foot drill up, and held it to the face where it had been marked for me, pushed the air control lever forward to set the machine off.

The first thing that happened was that the drill steel was all over the place. I couldn't hold the thing still long enough to start a hole, if I thought this was bad enough there was more to come—I had not turned on the air control lever for the air leg, and by this time the drill steel had lodged itself and had begun to sink into the rock. Without warning the machine dropped to the floor. I had the good sense to let the machine go, otherwise I might have done myself an injury. Why had I suddenly forgotten all that I had been told? Oh well, pick the machine up and start again. It was even heavier to lift from the ground than I had expected, but I lifted it up, and this time checked the air leg was set well into the loose rock on the floor. Having done this, I lifted the drill steel in my left hand, placed it carefully on one of Nipper's marks, turned the air control for the air leg and felt the slight pressure as the leg pushed upward. For once I had done something right, the air leg I had placed just in the right spot, unknowingly, of course, but it is very important to get this right, and the lads had told me this–in my excitement to get going I just forgot. I turned the control on and off a couple of times to get the feel of it. Simple, why had I not done this the first time? I set the air leg control so I could feel the lift, I could also pull it down if I wished to. Still holding the drill steel in my left hand with the machine now nicely balanced on the air leg, I eased the air lever on the machine gently forward and the drill steel began to rotate slowly in my left hand. I found I could now easily hold the drill steel onto the mark. As the steel began to cut into the rock I felt more confident, and pushed the air control lever full forward. As the machine jumped into life in my hands, I had to adjust the air leg control quickly to balance the machine up. I had to hold on to the machine, make sure I had the angle correct for the hole, and as Nipper had told me – sink it up to the hilt, lad.

It really was a great feeling standing there holding that drilling machine with the noise in my ears as it hammered that drill steel into the rock face. By the time I had two thirds of the hole driven into the rock, I could hardly see for the dust; the exhaust ports blasting air out in front of my face took some of the dust away, but not enough to make any difference, although I didn't mind, I was as happy as a king. When I had driven the hole fully in, now came the fun part, pulling the drill steel out of the hole. It should be easy enough, I had watched Ronnie and Nipper do it a few times. I pulled the air control lever back till the drill steel was just to say rotating, and turned a small lever on the back of the machine just above the handle; this would blow air straight through the drill steel and clear the hole of dust and any small chippings, simple. The blast of air cleared the hole all right, but I couldn't get the drill steel to come out. I pulled as hard as I could, and the sweat poured out of me. I suddenly realised, I had not turned the air off the air leg. After turning the air off the air leg, the leg was to lift clear of the floor and push back to its full extent. I then stood close up to the machine, took hold of the drill steel with my left hand, eased the air control forward slightly to keep the drill steel rotating, and with my right hand on the handle, pushed backwards, and the drill came out of the hole.

I picked myself up off the floor and stood looking at the machine as it lay there, the air leg had slid along the floor when I had pulled the drill out. I looked around to see if the lads had been watching, I had no need to worry on that score, they knew fine what I would be like, and had merely left me to find out for myself. I sat on the floor and wiped the sweat from my face, took my helmet off and dried my hair, I could feel my overalls sticking to me. Don't think much to this drilling job, I found myself thinking. Being a determined sort of bloke, I picked myself up, lifted the machine up, set the air leg, put the drill steel on the next mark, pushed the control lever and bored the hole with no trouble at all. That shift I put five holes in for Nipper and was very pleased with myself. Not too bad for a first time, I heard the lads say, when they came to see how I had performed, big smiles all over their faces. 'Has it been raining?' I heard one of them say. 'You're all wet, right down your back!' And we all sat on the floor and laughed as I recalled drilling those five holes. I realised as I sat there, the only way to learn was to get on and do the job, there being a lot more to it than I had thought.

By the end of that week, I had learned something of the drilling job, and

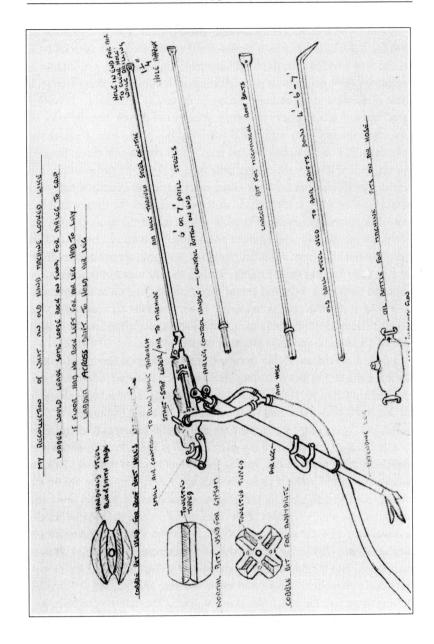

it would stand me in good stead for later on in my mining career. I could now manage to drill nine holes. The following week I would be working in another part of the mine, and would not be able to try my hand at drilling for a little while, but I had been to see John again, the man in charge, and asked to be put on the list for a driller's job if one should come available. He promised to put me on the list. In the meantime I had been sent to work in another part of the mine closer to the main heading. I would be driving the old drott, a tracked vehicle, or as the fitters and I called it, the knacked vehicle. Having said that, it was quite a useful vehicle to have in a mine like ours, very good for cleaning and levelling roads, something that had to be done on a regular basis. The place where I would be working with the drott would be the old forty-four district, and my first job using the drott would be to push rock that had been fired on the higher level, over a ledge that had been fired as a bench. A ramp had been made of fired rock, this enabled us to get up onto the higher level. The ramp had been built to one side of the workings, I had to drive the drott up the ramp to get to where I would be pushing rock over the bench to the lower level; rock that had been fired by the previous shift in the drifts on the upper level. The drott was a slow machine to work with after using the Hough 30, but I soon got into my stride. I had taken the advice of Johnnie the foreman and first tipped a bucket or two of rock close to the edge of the bench I was tipping over. The reason for this was quite simple, as I drove up to the edge of the bench to tip I could not see too well as I raised the bucket. The little heap of rock I had tipped told me when I was as close to the edge of the bench as I wanted to be, and when I felt the tracks run up onto the heap I only had to roll the bucket over to tip and I was on my way back for another bucketful. It did not take long before I had almost filled up the bench I had been tipping over. The loader on the shift was taking rock from another bench close by, with his Hough 30, the rock he was loading had been pushed over the bench by the previous shift. I stopped the drott, and climbed down. I could hear a drilling machine going but as yet had not been able to see it. I decided to take a look while letting some of the diesel fumes in the drift I had been working in clear; the fumes could make you feel quite dizzy after a while, working in them. I should point out all the diesel vehicles had to have a special scrubber fitted to the exhaust system. While these worked quite well, fumes were still emitted, and could, and indeed did, at times cause discomfort to those working in them.

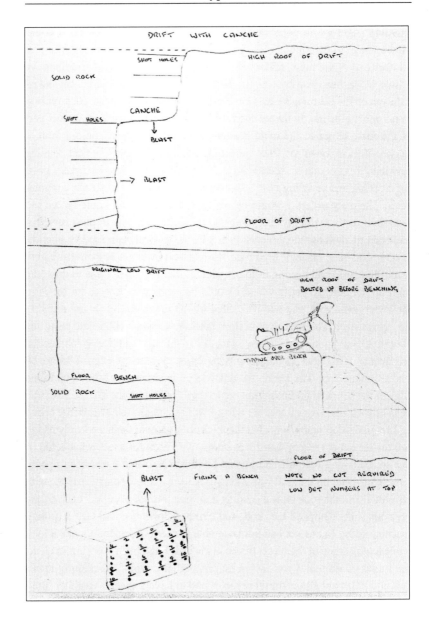

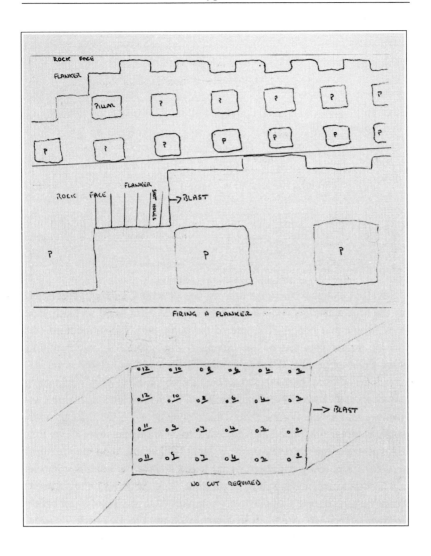

FIRING A FLANKER

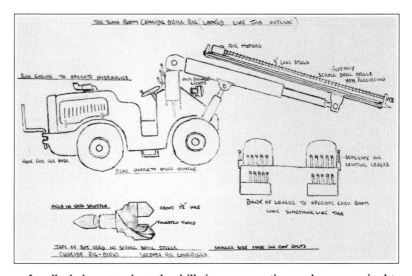

I walked along to where the drill rig was operating, and was surprised to say the least when I saw it. This was the Chaside I had heard so much about from Ronnie and Nipper. The size of the thing, twin booms mounted on a Chaside tractor, now this was something. It was quite noisy, two rock drills going at the same time. Dennis, the lad on the machine, looked at me as I entered the drift but was having to concentrate very hard on what he was doing, and didn't stop. I stood watching, fascinated by the machine, and by the way Dennis could handle it. One thing I liked straight away, the lighting on the machine, on the other hand the engine had to be left ticking over all the time, this was to run the hydraulic pump, to work the hydraulics on the machine. I must say I was really impressed by the speed it could put holes in compared to a hand machine, and watching Dennis operating the levers on this machine was something else, it all looked very complicated to me. I had to get back to my own job now so with a last look at the drill rig, I hurried back. I couldn't stop myself thinking about that drill rig for the rest of the shift. It seemed to me at the time the old drott spent more time broken down that it did actually working, and I know for a fact, it always seemed to me to break down when I had to use it. I only had to walk up to it, and something would go wrong with it, but it was an old machine and had had a hard life in the mines, long before I came on the scene, if that was any consolation to me.

At this time I was moving around a lot and not liking it too much, but had to put up with it; anyway, the main heading at this time wasn't too far from the bottom bait cabin, I was beginning to find my way around Birks Mine now, and finding it to be a very interesting place. Birks Mine had another entrance to it that I had as yet never seen, or had to use, it being situated on the Long Marton side. This had been the only way into the mine until the connecting drift had been driven through to Stamphill Mine, the drift from the mine entrance had been driven down at about one in eight. A right hand turn at the bottom of the hill would take you into the workings producing gypsum at the time I was there, and the bait cabin in use at that time. From the bottom of the hill from the mine entrance, the road carried on uphill into the old workings; here, white rock had been mined in the early days of the mine, known by the lads as the white rock area. To me it sounded like an interesting place to see, if I ever had the opportunity. The haulage metals were still in place and used regularly at that time, all the tractors and the drill rig had come in that way. In order to bring those machines into the mine, they had been taken apart on the surface, brought down on bogeys, and put together again down the mine. I would later be assisting in doing the very same job with another tractor myself. I should mention, on the surface at this time the old Aerial Ropeway sheds were still up, from where gypsum rock had been sent over to the mill, and one day when I had looked in there, the old cradle for rolling the tubs over to empty them and the weigh scale were both still there. When the connecting drift had been driven through and belts put in to Stamphill this had all become redundant but the ropeway was maintained in working condition.

It would be about this time I had some luck. I was told by the foreman I was to go drilling; I could hardly contain my excitement, and could not wait for the next shift coming round to get started. I would be sent with a very experienced man I knew as Jimmy. He would teach me how to drill and charge a drift, we would be working in drifts down in the main heading. I would be on six weeks' trial; at the end of that time, if I were any good, I would be on driller's bonus, this being the top grade of pay in the mines. Jimmy took me into my drift, marked it for centre, measured and marked the drift sides for me, and explained very carefully the angles at which I should bore the shotholes, and the reason for the angles in the cut. This had already been explained to me by Nipper and Ronnie, when I had first had a go at drilling. I listened very carefully to what Jimmy had to say to me for I knew he was a man of very few words, he would not be inclined to repeat himself. The idea had been to get at least half the drift bored by first bait, I had not had to bar the drift down this time, it had already been done for me. I watched as Jimmy had marked the drift up, the centre mark had been taken using two reflective markers hanging from the roof further up the drift we were in. Taking up the pick he placed the head of the pick onto the centre mark in the drift, horizontal to the face; using a red crayon he made a mark at the end of the pick shaft, turned the pick over and made another mark on the other side of the centre mark the same as the first. That's your cut. The pick shaft being two foot six long, made the cut holes five feet apart. Jimmy explained to me I would start the hole off at the outside mark and bore the shothole in towards the centre mark, the ends of the cut holes should preferably end up about eighteen inches apart. When the cut holes had been put in we would have a nice wedge shape.

He then took hold of the stemming stick we already had in the drift, placed one end of it on the centre mark in the horizontal position, and using a mark already cut on the stemming stick, measured off eight feet and made a mark. Having done the same on the other side of the drift, we now had a drift sixteen feet wide, it would also be about twelve feet high, or near enough. Jimmy put marks where I had to bore the holes then stepped up to the face, and put his leg against it and checked the height of one of the marks on the bottom row. 'See that,' he said to me, pointing with his finger at the mark at his knee, 'that's about the right height to start your bottom holes off, so you won't leave a step in the drift when it's fired, or a hole in the floor, okay lad.' He then walked off to get on with his own drift.

When I had clocked on at the start of the shift I had been handed a det box, this would be my det box, now I had started as a driller. The det box had been placed in a safe place out of the way in the drift, it would be my responsibility to look after it and see it was always in a safe place and locked, until the time came for me to use it. I took up the machine and surprised myself by getting half of my drift bored by bait time. The lads had given me a shout to let me know it was bait time, I stood there covered in white dust looking somewhat like a snowman, the dust was caked on my face due to the amount of sweat I had lost. I saw a few smiles as I walked into the bait cabin, and smiled to myself thinking, at least I had bored half

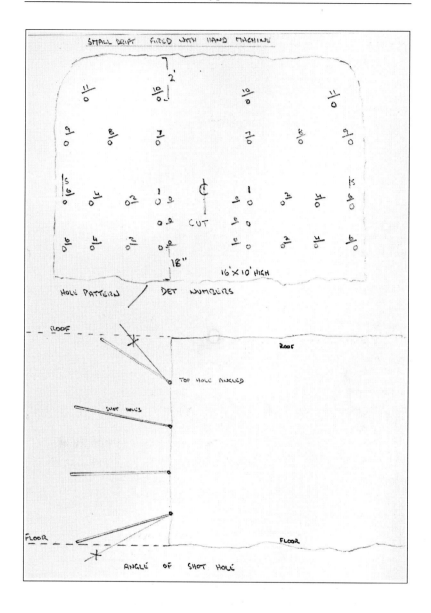

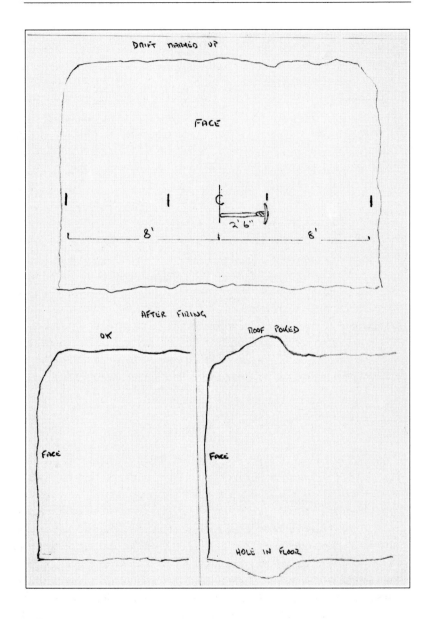

my drift on. I had to put up with a bit of good natured bantering but I didn't mind in the least, I had got what I had always wanted, I was now drilling. Jimmy came into my drift after bait and had a look at the holes. He knew I had had a go at drilling before. 'Try to keep the side holes straighter, or you will end up with a drift twenty feet wide,' was all he said. 'Let me know when you have finished and ready to charge, and I will come round.'

The roofs of the drifts were flat, and I had saved the top holes till last. The top holes had to be put in very carefully; if the holes were in too far the roof would be ruined, the idea being to fire the roof off the same bed as far as possible. I set the hole off about two foot below where I wanted the hole to finish, it was a good roof and I was frightened I might spoil it, the roof in this drift was a thick white bed, or layer of satin spar, and I would be aiming for this white bed as I drilled the hole. I watched very carefully as the drill steel sunk into the rock, deeper and deeper through the beds until I saw the dust pouring out of the hole suddenly change from almost grey-black to white. I knew then I had hit the white bed I had been going for and stopped the machine. After I had bored the other three holes the same, I put the machine to one side and went off to tell Jimmy. I was surprised when I saw he had not only bored his drift, but had almost finished charging it, and had bored half a drift on as well. It took all the puff out of me, I thought I had done well and had not wasted any time, I really was deflated.

Firing a drift

I watched as Jimmy finished wiring his drift up, and tried hard to take in the numbers of the dets in each hole, while waiting, but it was no use, I would need to be shown how it was done. 'Come on then, let's get your drift charged.' Jimmy had finished his drift, so off we would go to do mine now, I opened my det box. 'I will prod the holes for you, and you det up,' he said. I pulled out the prodder I had been given by the man in charge of the powder and dets on the surface, Old Gillie, a nice old chap. I used my prodder to lift the dets out of the sections provided for them in the det box. The dets were a tight fit in the sections and it was easier to get them out using the brass prodder. I pulled out the dets as Jimmy called out the numbers. Zeros for the cut, twos for the holes next to the cut, four and six and so on, until we had the bottom half of the drift done. I had wondered, but had not liked to ask, how we were to charge the top holes, as I knew I couldn't reach them without a ladder. With the bottom part now finished, and the only holes left to charge being four across the top, Jimmy took a stick of powder, or pill as we called them, put the det in the end as with the others, but this time carefully opened the opposite end to that which had the det in it. He then pushed the opened end of the pill onto the end of the stemming stick, pulled the wire out from the det and pushed it up the top hole, doing the same with all the other pills and stemming.

Simple when you know how, and now the drift was charged. All I had to do to complete the job, was connect the det wires together, starting at one end of the drift, and finish off at the other. When the drift had been charged and wired up, we now had a single length of wire at each side of the drift, to each of these a reel of shot firing wire would now be connected. To finish the job off the two reels of shot wire would then be run out to a safe distance, preferably at the back of a pillar. Once there, a very short length of insulation would be stripped off each reel of shot wire, each wire would then be connected to the circuit tester; by using the tester we could detect any fault in the circuit through the dets in the round of shots in the face, before attempting to fire the drift. The drift tested out okay, and I was very pleased about that, so was Jimmy. I had taken so long to finish drilling my drift we were running late. I also had the air to turn off, the air pipe to roll up after I had carried the machine out of the drift and placed it in a safe place, out of line of the shots, with the pick and stemmer.

By this time the full-time shotfirer, who charged those drifts drilled with the Chaside drill rig, had come to see what the hold up was. He had already checked the area, all the miners had set off on their way to the surface, only we now remained in this part of the mine. Now the lad who did the shotfiring had already checked the area out, we were clear to fire. From the drifts we now took the reels of shot wire, one reel into Jimmy's drift, to connect his drift up with mine, the two remaining reels we ran out to the main firing cable suspended from the roof, and from there we walked to the firing point. The firing point was actually the place where the five main firing cables for this part of the mine all came together. Each cable had a ticket attached to it, on each of the tickets drift numbers were written so the shotfirer knew exactly which drifts he would be firing from the firing point.

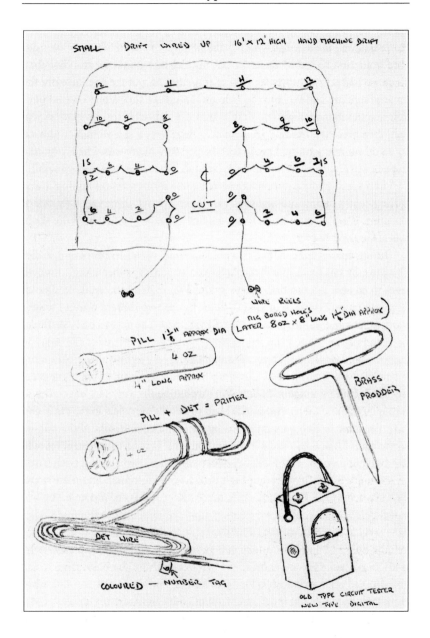

Jimmy wired ours up to the exploder, or battery as it was called by the lads. He passed me the key for winding the battery up. 'Here you go,' he said, 'fire your first round of shots.' I put my det box down for the first time since we had left the drifts for fear of forgetting it, put the key, actually the battery winding handle, into the hole on the side of the battery. 'Wind until you see the indicator glow,' Jimmy told me, 'shout 'Fire' as loud as you can, then press the button.' Immediately there was a sharp crack, followed by a dull rumbling noise. I could feel the pressure in my ears. I had forgotten to open my mouth as Jimmy had advised me. No matter, this was something I had dreamed of doing years ago, when I had read books on mining. I was feeling really happy and pleased with myself as we made our way out of the mine, I had actually fired, this would be something to tell my wife about when I arrived home.

During the training period I would have to spend to become a driller shotfirer, or shooter as they were then known, among other things, I would have to be able to det a drift up correctly. This took a little while to sink in. It would be explained to me many times by the two drillers whom I was to work with while training, but in the end I learned. The dets all had a different coloured tag on them, each tag a number telling the user what the delay in milliseconds would be. To explain this simply, a zero would go off before a number two, a two before a number four, and so on up to the highest det we used, being a number fifteen. This would be the very last det to fire in a round of shots. To charge a drift I had to put the zero dets in the cut holes, then the number two dets followed by the number four dets, and so on up to the roof. If the roof were a low flat roof, with four holes across it, I would use two number elevens in the two inner holes, and two number twelve dets in the outer holes. If it were a high drift to fire rig bored, and there were, say, six holes in it, I would put a number fifteen det in the top hole, the two holes below that would have number fourteen dets in, and the three holes below them could have three number thirteen dets in, or one twelve in the middle hole and number thirteen dets in the outer holes. I soon picked it up, and after I had done the job for the six weeks, John the boss came to see me. He had already talked to the other drillers before he saw me and asked how they had assessed me. Could I do the job safely, did my drilling come up to the minimum standard, did I understand how to charge correctly and if I was good enough for the job, or just a wanker. A shotfirer working and

44

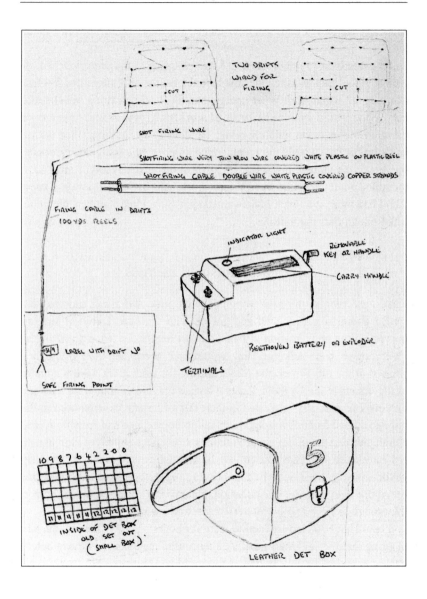

TWO DRIFTS
WIRED FOR
FIRING

. CUT . CUT

SHOT FIRING WIRE

SHOTFIRING WIRE VERY THIN KROU WIRE COVERED WHITE PLASTIC ON PLASTIC REEL

SHOTFIRING CABLE DOUBLE WIRE WHITE PLASTIC COVERED COPPER STRANDS

FIRING CABLE IN DRIFTS
100 YDS REELS

INDICATOR LIGHT

REMOVABLE
KEY OR HANDLE

CARRY HANDLE

LABEL WITH DRIFT N°

BEETHOVEN BATTERY OR EXPLODER

TERMINALS

SAFE FIRING POINT

10 9 8 7 6 4 2 2 0 0

5

INSIDE OF DET BOX
OLD SET OUT
(SMALL BOX)

LEATHER DET BOX

45

handling explosives and dets only makes a mistake once, he won't make two.

He came over to me in the drift I was charging at the time, watched for a short while, then he asked me how I would test the drift after I had finished charging it? I told him. What precautions did I take at firing time? I told him. What would I do in the event of a misfire? I was asked a number of other questions to do with charging. He didn't say anything, then with a smile on his face he told me I would be going onto the full grade G, bonus, this being the highest in the mines, as from the next pay day. I must have mumbled something like thanks very much, and he walked away. I knew then I had made it to what I had wanted ever since I had started at the mine, I had finally become a driller.

Old workings and cavities

I had now been at the mine something like nine and a half months, had settled down to it very well and got on with the lads. I always took an interest in the conversation at bait time but especially when some of the older miners were talking. They would talk about the time when they worked at the old Silverband Mine, mining for lead; there were a number of the miners at the Gypsum Mines who had previously mined for lead and barytes. I was mostly interested in their talk of natural caverns deep in the old Silverband Mine. I was still keen on potholing, and had recently joined a club, the Red Rose Cave and Potholing Club. The potholing club had an old farmhouse on High Casterton fell, near Kirkby Lonsdale where they would meet for their potholing and caving trips at weekends. As yet I had only been over there on one occasion, but any talk of caves, or any hole in the ground for that matter, interested me, and I would be all ears.

I could have sat and listened to them for hours on end if I could, the talk of firing into the 'old man's drifts', a term used meaning the miners before our time, and of finding in one of these old workings the old man's tools just as he had left them, he had not returned. How they would sometimes slip into the natural caverns in the mine just to have a look around, but they did not stray too far in them, it was too easy to get lost. In fact it was a very good workmate of mine, Roland, who told us about the time he himself had lost his way in the caverns, when he had worked at the Silverband Mine. It had been towards the end of his shift, with a little time to spare, he had decided he would see these caverns for himself. He told us he slipped into the caverns through a crack in the side of one of the drifts, and started to have a look around. He had been so taken with the caverns, the size and the passages leading off all over the place that he had not taken careful note of where he was, and realised he was totally lost in the caverns. He had wandered around for some time, looking for a way out, getting more and more worried, when looking into one of the passages he thought he could just see daylight in the distance. He said how he had fair run towards it. It had been daylight, he had been lucky it had not been dark outside or he would never have found his way out. When he came to the hole where he could see the daylight, it had only been quite a small hole, and he had to make the hole big enough for him to get through with his hands. The hole where he had emerged had been some considerable distance over the back of the Dunfell, the actual mine entrance being on the Dufton side of the fell.

Roland was kind enough to take myself and a close friend up the fell on one occasion to see if we could find the location of that hole. We did not find the hole, it being a big area to search in so little time, but we did find around four places we thought would 'go', as we used to say in potholers' terms. They gave every indication, by their position on the fell. I noticed a blast of warm air coming up through the holes in the rocks that we looked into, but most noticeable of all to the three of us, being miners, was the smell of old mine workings. We made a note of all the more interesting places on the fell for a return visit. I knew from past experience at finding old mines in the Scoredale area, winter could be a help in finding them. During the winter months, on a cold frosty morning and also when the ground is covered in snow, it is sometimes possible to observe as I had done, warm air rising, especially from a large cavity in the ground such as a mine, as steam into the atmosphere. Although I might add to that, many of the holes found in this way were too small to make entry into them possible.

At this point I feel I should make it quite clear, there were those amongst the lads I worked with who thought all cavers, potholers and the like should be locked away in a safe place and left there. There were also those like Roland who had worked in the old Silverband Mine, and were interested to hear about my visits into caves and the local old lead and barytes workings. I would tell of the old iron wedges found, and the old tallow candle stuck into a handful of clay on the side of an old man's drift, the ancient bucking iron found by my mate Fred, and the clog imprint in a drift that had filled with calcite.

During the time I spent learning to drill and shotfire in the Birks Mine, I had been told to beware of hitting a cavity whilst boring the shotholes. I had heard talk of them but as yet had not seen one. At this time the drilling would be done with both hand machines and the Chaside drill rig, the men on the hand machines charged their own drifts, the man on the Chaside had only to put the holes in the drift for charging. This allowed the rig to move quickly around the empty drifts and bore them ready for the lad employed on full-time charging, thus keeping a plentiful supply of rock lying in the drifts ready for loading.

The charger at that time, Tommy, knew of a cavity and offered to show it me, the cavity being quite close to the bait cabin on the road back to the fitting shop. I crawled through the hole into the cavity, and stood up on a pile of rock in the middle of it. I looked up, it must have been all of thirty feet in height and at least twenty feet across at the bottom, conical in shape almost to a point at the top, and the sides were very rough with sharp edges. How it got there in all the solid rock around it, I can't say. We crawled back through the hole, into the drift. I had a good look at the rock face on the outside, it would have been impossible to tell just by looking at it that only a few inches of rock had separated the driller from that cavity as he had bored his holes. I would hit cavities myself in the years ahead but not all as the one I have just described. Some would make so much water that a pump would need to be installed to stop the water from flooding the workings. The shape of some of the cavities would vary also, instead of the typical conical shape, others I looked into at a much later date were very low, flat and wide inside and could run to as much as sixty feet, with some water.

One of the last cavities I looked into that I remember very well, was in Longriggs Mine, in the old workings at the back of the bunker. The cavity itself had been typically conical in its shape, it had been fired into very near to the top of the cone, and water was being made. The initial hole that had been fired into the cavity would be enlarged, a pump set up at this hole, a

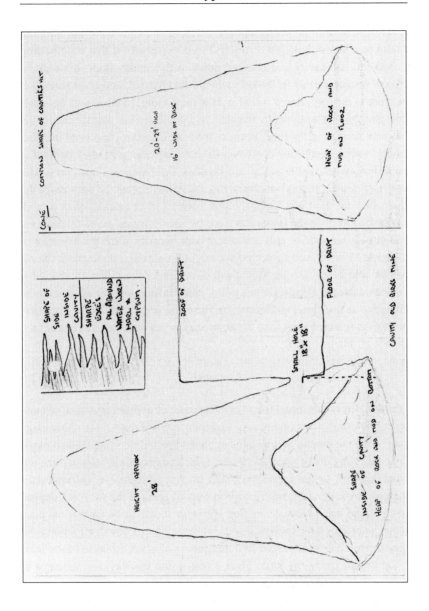

CONE

COMMON SHAPE OF CAVITIES MET

2.0' - 2.8' HIGH

16' WIDE AT BASE

HEIGHT OF ROCK AND MUD ON FLOOR

SHAPE OF SIDE INSIDE CAVITY

SHARPE CONE'S

ALL AROUND WATER WORN MARL & GYPSUM

HEIGHT APPROX 28'

ROOF OF DRIFT

FLOOR OF DRIFT

SMALL HOLE 18" x 18"

SHAPE INSIDE OF CAVITY

HEAP OF ROCK AND MUD ON BOTTOM

CAVITY OLD BLACK MINE

pipe dropped into the cavity through the hole and allowed to run until the cavity was almost emptied of water. I took the liberty at that time to drop a rope into the cavity and climbed down to the muddy floor. It would be around sixteen feet up to the hole where I had entered, and another ten feet or more to the roof. It was full of mud at the bottom. I looked into the water in a passage that went off to one side, and could see the passage carried on but was flooded to the roof. Because it became known I had been into this cavity, a wire mesh was bolted over the hole, a pump had to be left running on a float switch and is, as far as I know, still running as I now write. The only cavities the miners concerned themselves with were the ones under the floor. Not too far away from the one I have just described, quite a large cavity had been found under the floor by sheer chance probe drilling; we had already decided to pull out of that area because of the poor quality of the rock. When it was suspected we might hit a cavity, the man on the rig would bore holes into the floor, and down under the pillars to check for cavities. I should mention at this point, probe drillers were employed by the company at that time, and came into the mine when required to make test borings in selected areas, and the holes they bored were in hundreds of feet.

Crystals

I think it was at this time I found my first piece of gypsum crystal or selenite by pure chance. I was on my way to the surface walking up the old haulage route from the bunker bottom in Stamphill Mine. After riding the belt down the connecting drift from Birks Mine, I decided on walking through the old Durhams drift to get to the main belt by way of a door at the tandem. I walked down the drift, taking a good look at parts of the roof as I walked and noticed one or two holes that appeared to me to be natural cavities, rather than shot hole sockets. In one of these holes I could see among the clay in the hole what looked like tiny pieces of glass. I realised then what I had found. Using my knife blade I poked into the clay and managed to remove one small piece without damage. There it was in my hand, a small but perfect crystal, I just could not believe my luck, after all this time searching I had found what I always knew I would find if I looked hard enough. I already had a few interesting rock samples at home that I had

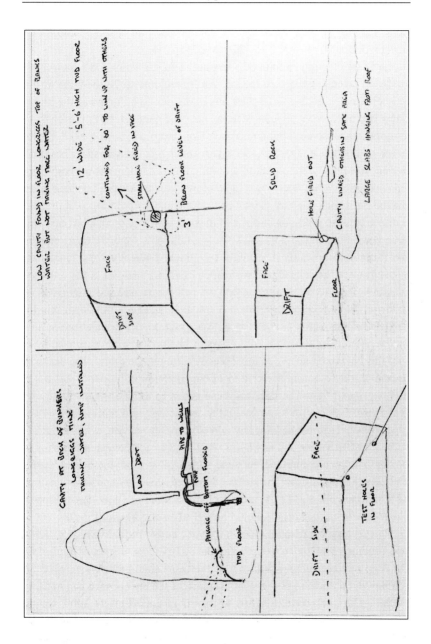

collected locally over the years, but this piece to me was something very special. I would treasure it for the rest of my life.

Later on during my time as a gypsum miner I would find many more pieces of selenite for my collection, but it would never be the same as that very first piece. There were other pieces of rock to be found in the mines, daisy bed being very popular with the lads, the name given to it because of its appearance, some salmon pink in colour covered in what looked like the heads of flowers, and they did look very much like daisy heads. The colour varied, from the salmon pink to a dark red brown, some almost black, and my favourite white rock with light brown flower heads. The lads often picked out a nice piece of daisy bed to keep, and I would imagine in many a miner's house even now a piece of daisy bed will be on display, and very nice too. I once asked how thick the gypsum beds were we now mined, I had been told upwards of seventy feet thick, I already knew below the gypsum were the sandstone beds. What I had not realised at the time was just how close to the sandstone bed we actually mined and how close we came to the surface on occasions. A test hole had been put down into the sandstone beds and a pipe left in with a gauge to check water pressure; it had registered sixty pounds of pressure. I had not been too surprised when told this but would keep it in mind when drilling in the future. The lads who did the test hole boring had told us of one exploratory hole they had put in at Longriggs Mine. The hole had been put in to around two hundred plus feet when they realised they had hit a cavity; they put more tubes on and pushed them in to see how far it would be across the cavity; it was estimated to be all of fifty feet. All test holes were sealed with cement when the test boring had been completed. In some parts of the mine, the boreholes that had been put down from the surface were occasionally exposed on the side of a pillar after firing. Later safety regulations did not allow this to happen. Boreholes from the surface would be left in a solid block of rock.

By this time I had settled down to work at the Birks Mine very well. I had become accustomed to the long hike up to the mine from Stamphill via the nine belt connecting drift, but at the same time I always enjoyed the journey out at the end of the shift. Because of the distance we had to travel to the surface we obviously had to set off in good time to allow for the distance. Myself and two others usually walked from the bottom of nine belt and followed the metals up the old haulage road, this would take us through the old workings on our way out of the mine. It had been my two companions who had shown me the short cut through these old workings to the main belt, where I had found my small piece of selenite.

One day on the way out, they took me to see one of the very early bait cabins. It had been in these workings where a hole had appeared in the roof after firing at one time; I would see that hole myself at a later date. The bait cabin had been made in a cut through using wood for a framework, covered with hessian, no door. We found in the drift at the back of the cabin, the remains of a clog and also the remains of an old carbide lamp, it had been a large hand held lamp. If we had tried to pick the lamp up it would have fallen to pieces, what carbide had been left in the lamp had obviously contributed to its condition; there were also some very damp but still recognisable cigarette packets. When I first began to visit caves I had purchased a carbide lamp, it had fitted onto my helmet and I had used it many times. I would not have liked to have had to work in the mine using one. I thought of the old time miners using tallow candles in the lead mines, and wondered what they would have said if they could have seen us with our modern cap lamps, helmets and rock drills.

The haulage system was at this time being used daily to bring in the blocks and sand, with cement for use in making the brattices being built in the Birks Mine. The explosive materials, spare parts and anything required for the two mines all had to be brought in using the tubs through a separate entrance at Stamphill Mine, and taken to Birks by way of nine belt. The men on this job were known as the spare gang. It amazed me the first time I saw these lads moving a load of sand and cement in the tubs, it was a long haul to the top of the nine belt from the surface. At the corner in the bunker bottom before they had come to the bottom of nine belt, three of the tubs came off the metals loaded with bags of cement. I looked and thought that would take time to sort out and asked if I could be of help. 'No thanks, we will soon have them back on,' they said. Using a couple of short bars they had with them in the tubs and some large pieces of rock from the side of the belt, they had those tubs back on the metals in minutes.

I would very soon have another opportunity to visit the old workings where I had found my piece of selenite in the Durhams district, whilst working a maintenance shift. Four or more of us had been sent to what the lads called the Cockloft, with two fitters to recover an old scraper. These

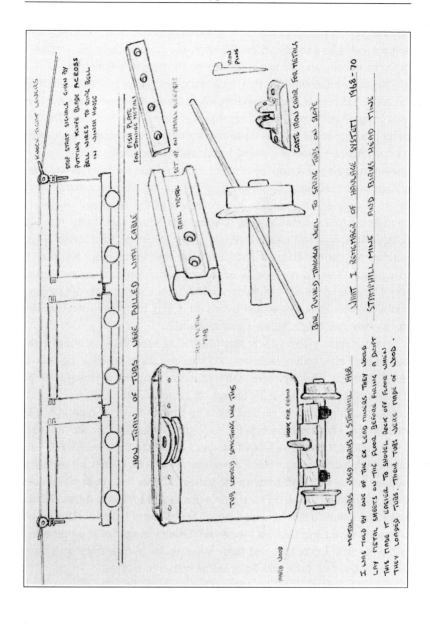

had been used in the mines before the front-end loaders now in use, to remove the fired rock from the drifts, the scraper being no more than a winch with a continuous cable, the cable running through a block hooked into a steel ring swinging loosely in a hole in the end of a steel pin with one flat side to it. This pin would be placed in a hole bored in the drift for it at a chosen point, a steel wedge then being hammered in tight on the flat side of the pin to lock it in place. The man on the winch would run out a small bucket or scraper attached to the steel cable into the drift, and using the levers to control the winch, pull the bucket or scraper, now full of rock, back towards him on the winch. The scraper as it was called had been set up on one side of the belt used to take the rock away; as the bucket of rock was pulled towards the belt, it would ride up a small ramp of rock placed there for this purpose. A steel plate with two side plates welded on to stop spillage, bolted to the belt structure, would allow the rock to be fed onto the belt.

To get to the place where the old scraper was we passed through the Durhams district on our way to the upper workings, or as the lads called it, the Cockloft. This district had been mined over old workings. When our work had been completed I had another look in the Durhams for some more selenite, and as luck would have it I found one more very small piece. As for the scrapers, the only time I was ever to use one had been on the stockpile at the back of the bunkers.

Things were always changing at the mines, nothing ever seemed to me to stay the same for long, men starting, men leaving, men being moved around the mines. What we probably didn't realise at the time was that all these changes were due to the fact that, from the year I had started in the mines, 1968, British Gypsum had been building another automated plasterboard factory at an estimated cost of over two and a half million pounds to make it one of the biggest of its kind in Europe. There would be at least four hundred men employed there at this time in the plant, and it was said another hundred would be wanted. It was estimated that something like thirty-five million square yards of plasterboard would be produced annually when the new plant was running.

Very shortly now I would be using a hand machine for the last time, that is for boring a drift. Drill rigs were the thing now; hand machines, apart from odd bits of jobs, would be almost a thing of the past. When I thought

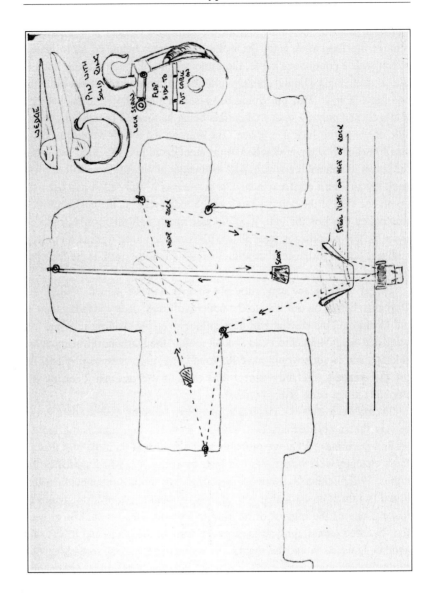

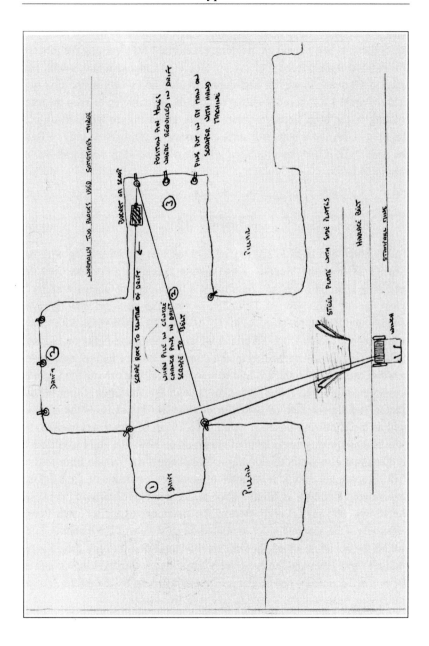

back on the short time I had used one I had to smile to myself at all the tricks the lads had played on me during the time I was learning the job: the oil that had been poured into my air tube at the machine end, which had sprayed all over me when I had started to bore holes with it; the first two or three drifts I had bored, fighting to hold the machine up to keep the steel rotating in the hole, because someone had turned my air tap halfway off; the times I carried a new drill steel all the way from outside only to find, the next shift, it had been replaced with an old one—this would all be the past to me now.

Chaside rig

The foreman had been to see me, he told me I would be drilling with the Chaside as from the Monday. I had always fancied a go on the Chaside, well now I would have the opportunity. I was very apprehensive about it when the day came around, I climbed up onto the machine, now this was something different for sure, the air hoses were three inch pipes with heavy brass screw fittings. I was surprised when checking the lights on the machine to find they were air driven self contained units. I had till now never heard of this type of light. I would have no difficulty in driving the Chaside around the mine, I had after all put my time in as a loader on a similar type tractor, and already had my ticket for driving diesel vehicles in the mine as well as my shotfiring ticket. It would take a shift or two to get used to the twin booms sticking out in front of the machine, however, and I would need to take great care while towing the air hose behind the vehicle from drift to drift. I took a good look at the rows of levers on each side of the machine and listened carefully as Ronnie gave me ten minutes tuition on the use of the levers, one set on each side of the machine to operate each boom separately. One separate lever, mounted on each side of the machine, controlled the speed at which the drill steel was pushed into the face. I soon realised these levers had to be set very carefully, or the drills would jam in the holes. To operate the machine I had to stand up on the tractor, out of the driving seat, with the steering wheel in front of me.

I should point out that the drills on this machine did not have percussion, as the hand machines did, but were rotary drills; they did not have a centre hole bored through the length of them, for air to blow through to clear the holes of dust. On this machine the holes were made using a nine foot long drill steel, the drills used were called scroll drills, something like a giant wood boring bit. As the drill turned in the hole, the tungsten carbide cutting bit in the end of the drill cut into the rock, and the dust and fine chippings would be forced back up the hole with the scroll shape of the drill and would form a nice little pile under the hole being drilled. I should also point out, the drifts being bored with the Chaside were on average around eighteen feet high, but could be even higher than this, the obvious advantage being the higher tonnage obtained when the drift is fired, compared with a drift fired with a hand machine. To explain this, the length of drill, nine feet large diameter shot hole, on the Chaside, to seven feet small diameter shot hole, hand machine, plus height of drift, twelve or so hand machine to eighteen plus Chaside. The Chaside also had the advantage that it could be driven from one drift to another very easily and from one end of the mine to the other without any trouble at all.

The controls had been explained to me, that is to say the levers to operate each boom. The lad who had instructed me left me with it, after he had explained the controls, saying the best way to learn was to get on and drill with it, learning by my own mistakes as I did. I would certainly learn by my mistakes, fortunately for me I did not make too many, the only problems I would have were in setting the drift up in the first place. I would mark the drift up from the centre mark as with other drifts, eight feet on each side of centre, but to get the angle of the cut just right I had to get off the machine and check very carefully. I had to remember the drills on this machine were nine feet long, and I did not want to sink them too far into the floor, but of course I would do, sooner or later. Also when drilling the side holes I had to check I did not let the drills run out into the pillar, they had to be kept straight at all times. The roof took me a little time to become accustomed to, normally with a Chaside drift I would fire the roof in an arch, but sometimes it would be necessary to fire it flat, or to leave what we called a canche, this would be drilled and fired the next time the drill rig was in that drift. Firing a roof in this way would bring rather more rock down, the reason for this being, the nine foot drills could be sunk right into the rock full length.

The pattern of holes for an arched roof would be as follows: one in the top dead centre, two under that followed by three under those two.

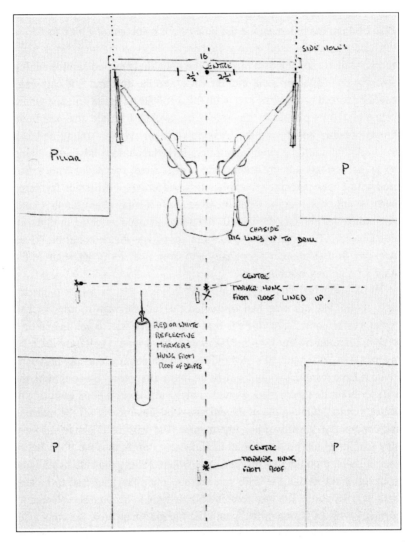

Remembering the drift underneath had already been fired, barred down, and loaded out, and drilled again, before drilling the roof, the drift and roof would be charged all at one go, to be fired together. When checking the drift after firing, you would find that although the roof had been seven feet or more behind the face of the drift, before firing, after firing the roof would almost have caught up with the face of the drift. This is because, with nothing underneath it when the roof was fired, it ripped the rock out way past the end of the shot holes in the roof, the problem with this being, the sides of the drift in the roof were really rough to bar down. On the plus side, what a pile of rock to load out, it was there for all of us to see now, hand drilling was almost at an end, machines would be the thing of the future, and we would just have to get used to the idea. I must just say the worst of the barring down and, in my opinion, some of the most dangerous, occurred when a drift had been fired, such as a cut through, for the very first time into a pillar side.

I would spend quite a while drilling with the Chaside and enjoyed every minute of it, once I had mastered the levers, and learnt how to repair a burst air hose. So much more rock could be fired in a Chaside drift. I was soon to drill my first bench, this being something I had been told about as a driller by Jimmy when I had first started, but until now had never had to do. The benches I would be drilling were in the old 44 area, where I had pushed over with the drott when I had first come to the Birks Mine; in fact they were indeed the very same benches. The drifts on the top had by now all been stopped. Once the benches had been fired out, that was it, we would pull the belts out and the area would be abandoned, but that is mining, moving on all the time. I took the Chaside into the area, it would be a week's work or so to get fired up. I set off to drill at one end, and would work my way along the row of benches. To drill a bench was simple enough, the height of these benches being about eleven feet high, I would start at the top and work down, three holes on each side from the centre and three rows each side top to bottom. The firing of the bench differed from firing a drift, the difference being, when firing a drift the most important thing was to fire the cut out first, the cut being the six bottom holes in the centre of the drift, that had been charged with the zero dets. If for any reason these shots did not fire, or had mistakenly been charged with high numbered dets, and the cut failed to fire out, you would almost certainly end up with a blowback. Definition of a blowback: a very loud bang, with the powder blowing back out of the holes, leaving about as much rock in the drift as could be loaded into a wheelbarrow.

There was no need to worry about a cut in a bench, the zero dets being placed into the top row of holes, number two in the next row down, ending up with the high numbered dets on the bottom instead of in the top; obviously the weak point was the top of the bench, this is where the zero dets would be placed. Since I had been drilling with the Chaside I had been lucky enough not to have had too many problems with poking the roofs or with leaving too many steps in the floor. The roof was easy to keep okay but I had to make sure the drills were absolutely level when I put them in to keep them that way. The floors were a different set up, to keep them level took a bit more doing; I would say it was just experience, and trial and error, no more than that.

Roof bolting

It would be about this time I was to get my first taste of roof bolting, having been at the mines almost two years now. Some of us in the younger end were always hungry for the overtime, while working the six to two, or early shift, we could work to four thirty in the afternoon, but had to be prepared to do whatever jobs required doing, roof bolting, belt cleaning, any job at all. I was told to go roof bolting with Ronnie. We would be bolting the area that Ronnie and Nipper were still drilling by hand, not far from the fitting shop. The bolting in that area being done the old way, this would be an experience I thought, and how right I was. First of all we had to collect the bolting gear, and air tubes, in a trailer that was hitched up to an old Ford 2000. Ronnie would drive the tractor into the drift to be bolted up, stopped with the trailer under the roof he had chosen to bolt, I was sent to connect the air pipe up to the nearest tap. When I came back Ronnie had set up what was no more than a scaffolding frame, on the back of the tractor. I gave him a hand to put a couple of planks across the top of this frame and he would climb up onto the planks. After checking to see they would not tip up when we stood on them, he asked me to pass up the stoping machine. The stoping machine was a fair weight to be lifting about, but eventually we had it on top of the scaffold, plus the bolts to go in and the drills for drilling the holes.

I climbed up onto the planks beside Ronnie. 'You can drill the holes,' he said, and put the stoper into my hands. I took hold of the stoping machine, and held it steady while Ronnie put the two foot drill into it. 'Off you go,' he said when the drill steel was in place. I had of course by this time had a

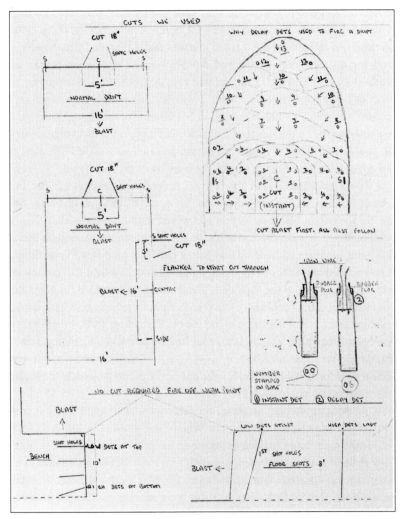

look at one of these machines before, and knew the controls. I turned the right hand control, and felt the stoper rise up on the airleg, until it touched the roof at the point where I had been told to drill the hole. With the drill pressing against the roof on the airleg I then pulled the air lever on the left hand side up and the drill began to rotate, slowly at first, until I pulled the lever fully up and the machine roared into life. The control lever for the airleg was all I had to alter as the drill sank into the roof; after the two foot, it was the four foot, the six foot, then the bolt and plate, put the dolly in the machine and tighten the nut up, and that was that. I thought I had done very well for my first bolt, and it had not been easy standing on planks on scaffolding at that height. I put the two foot drill in ready to start again; as soon as I had positioned the stoper, I was holding it with both hands as I pushed it to where I wanted it, when it fell clean over the side. A firm hand had grabbed me by the scruff of the neck. 'Let it go,' I heard a voice saying, 'if you had held on it would only have pulled you with it.' Oh well, I thought, as I climbed down to pick it up and start all over again.

I would put hundreds of bolts in over the following years as a miner, but I never had to do it on scaffolding like that again, thank God; that area, like the old forty-four, had seen its best and would soon be abandoned. I should point out right now we did have what we called our scaling carriage at Birks, this being a converted Bedford waggon; it had been modified by our fitters, it had an extendable boom mounted on the back that would lift and lower, and stabilising legs at the back end. These would be extended for when the boom was in use, it could also traverse to right or left. In all a very useful machine to us, it was also used to bar the big Chaside drifts down after they had been fired and it was used for roof bolting in the main heading area. I should say now, the roof bolting would only be done as and when it was required, at the Birks Mine bolts were not put in just to look nice, they were put in for safety purposes only.

Roof bolts could also be useful for other jobs, as I would find out later on, not just for holding the roof up. When I had worked in the Well Drift the airline pipes had not been put in along the pillar sides, but on the floor. This in itself made no difference in their use, but could be a nuisance to us when driving machines around, and of course they had been easier to install on the floor. Here at Birks they had also been put in on the floor, but things as always were changing and we had started to hang them from the roof; this is where the roof bolts could be used. To hang the heavy three inch steel pipes from the roof, holes would first be drilled using the stoper, spaced out at around seventeen foot along the pillar sides. The bolts would have been taken to the fitting shop to be heated and bent at the bottom to fit the pipes. Before the pipes could be hung up, the bolts would be put into the holes already drilled for them, and screwed up by hand into the holes,

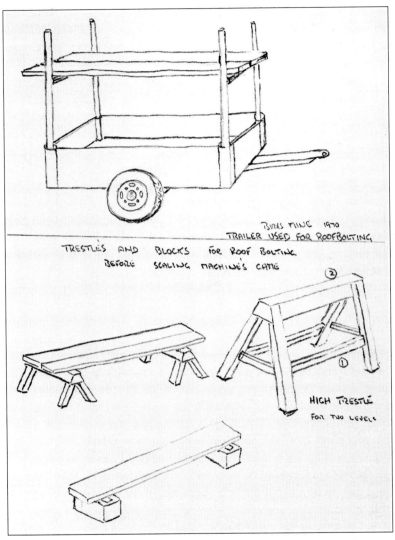

BIRDS MINE 1970
TRAILER USED FOR ROOFBOLTING

TRESTLES AND BLOCKS FOR ROOF BOLTING
BEFORE SCALING MACHINES CAME

②

HIGH TRESTLE
FOR TWO LEVELS

①

checking to see they were in a tidy line, and as close in to the roof as was possible, without having to bend the pipes. The pipes, which by this time had been spaced out along the pillar bottoms, could then be lifted with a tractor bucket up to the roof and hung on to the bolts. We found it was more convenient to us to have the pipes hung up in this manner than to have them on the floor, it was well worth the effort. The bolts would of course be used for a variety of jobs at times, from hanging airline pipes to holding vibrators to the floor, fastening belt end rollers to the floor, and in the fitting shops for bolting the heavy lifting gear to the roof.

I should point out, bolts were put in a suspect roof as a safety measure. We had been told, one bolt if put in place correctly, with the steel plate on the bottom, could hold something like ten or more tons. A year or two later, I would be standing in a drift looking at a vast pile of rock on the floor, that only the shift before had been a four way spot, and it had been bolted up about two years before it dropped out. Fortunately no one had been around or passing underneath at the time it had dropped in, bolts and all, but it had given us a great deal to think and talk about. During the time I had been drilling at Birks Mine, I had on only one occasion been asked to drill floor shots, and because there had only been a small number of shots to do I had put them in using a hand machine with air leg off; there was always a machine about if you required one.

Floor shots

I had been asked to put a whole lot of floor shots in, and I had to seek advice on what would be the best way to go about it. I had driven the Chaside into the area where the floor shots were to be drilled. I found it had already had some shots fired by the previous shift; this at least gave me a starting point in the drift. I lined the Chaside up in the centre of the drift and, lucky for me, one of the lads who had been sent to give me a hand, had done this before and knew the routine. The very first thing we had to do was to take our shovels and scrape all the loose rock off the surface to be drilled. Having done that we then had to tilt both the booms of the drill rig up in order to drill the shot holes. I would have to drill three holes on each side of the drift. I climbed up onto the Chaside, lifted the boom to make sure I had the right angle for the job; the second thing I should have done, but would now have to do anyhow, was to stuff some rag into the chuck fitting to stop the drills dropping out. Both drills had dropped out as soon as I lifted them clear of the floor. The angle for the holes would be near enough to forty-five degrees for the first row of holes, the second row just more than the first,

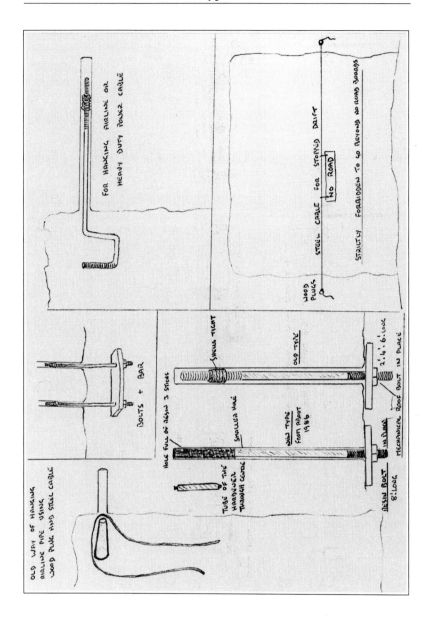

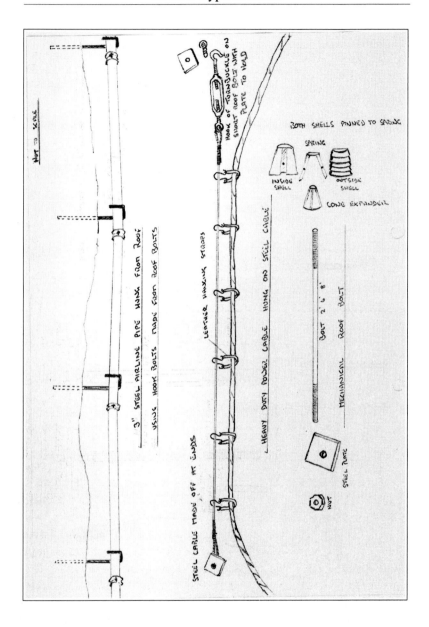

NOT TO SCALE

3" STEEL AIRLINE PIPE HUNG FROM ROOF

USING HOOK BOLTS MADE FROM ROOF BOLTS

HOOK OF TURNBUCKLE ON SHORT ROOF BOLT WITH PLATE TO HOLD

LEATHER HANGING STRAPS

STEEL CABLE MADE OFF AT ENDS

HEAVY DUTY POWDER CABLE HUNG ON STEEL CABLE

BOTH SHELLS PINNED TO SPRING

SPRING

INSIDE SHELL

OUTSIDE SHELL

CONE EXPANDER

BOLT 2' 6' 8'

MECHANICAL ROOF BOLT

STEEL PLATE

NUT

and the rest of the holes almost vertical. I began to drill the holes, the first two left a nice little heap of dust at the top of each hole, and these heaps of dust at the top of the holes would now act as markers as I put the rest of the holes in. I had to reverse the Chaside after each second row of holes, the lad with me moving the air hose as I did so. I worked my way back to the cut through, and finished the last row of holes in line with the pillar corner. I now had to reposition the drill rig in the four way and drill the next set of floor shots back toward where I had finished off the first set, and the set after that in the same way as the second set. The next shift in would start to drill where I had finished off the first set of floor shots, and if I had not fired all the holes, they would fire those also.

It was always nice to see the result of your drilling and charging efforts and I was no exception to this. We had always taken a pride in our work, and liked to think of ourselves, in the words of one of the lads, as the best, and I am quite sure we were the best. I think I can honestly say, we did have some terrific shots in the drifts, and the floor shots were a treat to look at, with some massive piles of rock, a real credit to those who worked with me in the mines at that time. The drifts would be kept pretty much on line, we would have the odd one that would get a bit off line on occasions, due mainly to men like myself, who lacked experience and did not always take enough care, being in too big a hurry to get the work done in the course of the shift.

As time passed and I became more experienced at the job, I did not panic so much as I had done at first; the more I drilled the better I would become at it, and also the easier it would get. I think this must apply to most jobs. I can say one thing: if you did make a hack up of it the lads would soon let you know in no uncertain terms, using some very quaint language, and rightly so. I had my share of right good bullings from the time I started, most of which I should say I had deserved, and in the course of time I would dish many a good bulling out myself. The miners at Kirkby Thore had come into mining from many walks of life, much the same as I had, many had come into mining from farm work, used to a bit of hard graft, rough and ready lads, full of fun. It always amazed me when we had a good crack in the bait cabin, what each man could do other than mining. We could talk about putting the roof on a house, drainage systems, gardening was always a favourite, plumbing, and mechanics, whatever, anything except politics,

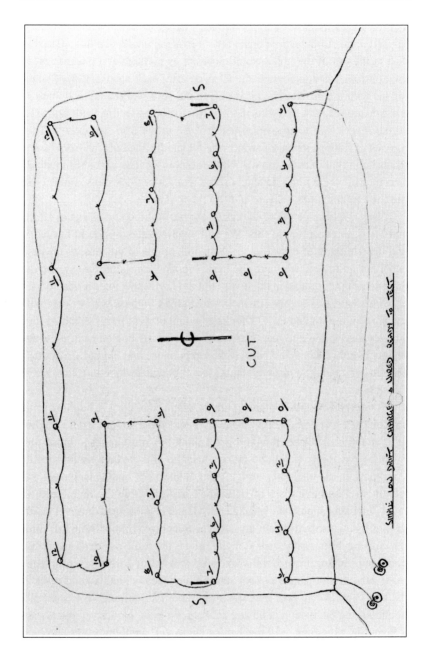

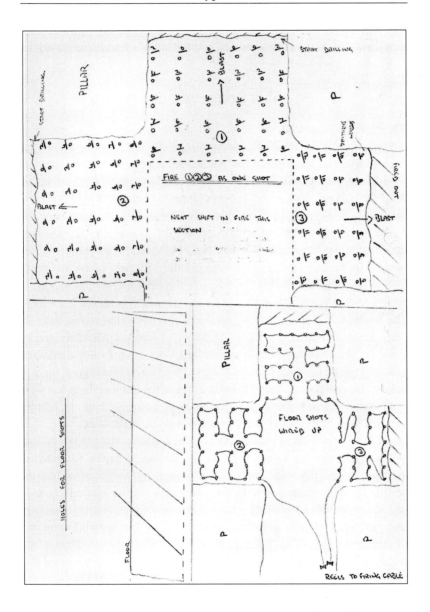

this was something they liked to keep to themselves, and just as well, politics always was a dirty word and best left out of sensible conversations.

Shot firing, full time

The shift foreman told me he wanted me to go on full-time charging. Tommy, the lad who had been doing it regularly for some time now, had decided to make a move, and had got himself a job with the coal board, at a coal mine near Doncaster. I didn't have much choice really, so I agreed to be the charger, or shotfirer, as I would now be known. What I had to do was to charge the drifts drilled on with the Chaside, and to take the powder round to the lads on hand machines, collect any powder they left and take it back to the underground reserve station. The shotfirer had plenty to think about with this job, and a lot of responsibility. He didn't have too much time to spare and from what I had seen of the other lad, always seemed to be in a rush to get on. My transport for the job would be an old Ford 2000. The tractor had a platform mounted over it, which would enable the man charging me to reach the top holes in the high Chaside drifts; this could be done by using the lightweight extending ladder, placed on the platform mounted on the tractor. I found that a head for heights was a good thing to have while charging the very top holes in the drifts. Another thing that went with the job: I had to carry two extra large det boxes with me at the start of shift, from Stamphill up the nine belt hill to the Birks Mine.

At the top of the hill I would pick up the tractor at the reserve station, this being an approved safe place for the storage of explosive materials underground. I would then load up the powder I required for myself for the shift in the trailer, along with the powder for the lads on hand machines. I would already have been told where to drop off the powder for the lads, and this could sometimes be a fair round trip for me, before I could get started on my own drifts. I would arrive at the drifts I had to charge, check to see if any were going to fire through, one into another on the other side of it; that is, if one would fire through, this meant I would have to make sure to fire these two together.

I would fire three full drifts on average in the shift, and I had to get a move on to get them finished. It was the top end or roof of the drift that

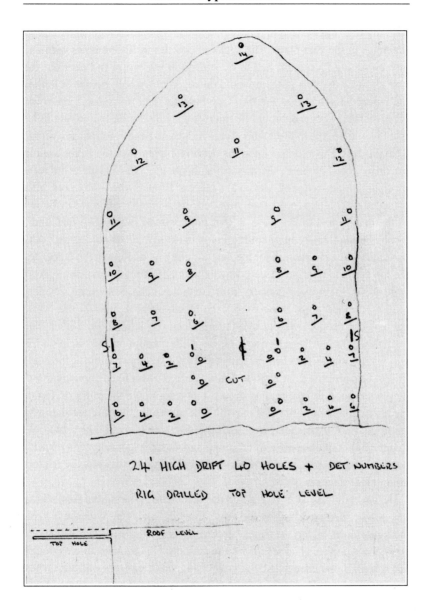

24' HIGH DRIFT 40 HOLES + DET NUMBERS

RIG DRILLED TOP HOLE LEVEL

ROOF LEVEL

TOP HOLE

took my time up, bearing in mind I had to use the ladder to get up to charge the holes in the first place. The sticks of powder to fill the holes with and any stemming I used, all had to be stuffed in the top of my overalls, the primers with the dets in them would be stuck in my belt, before I climbed the ladder—I sometimes felt like Guy Fawkes. The first thing I had to do when starting to charge would be to prick the pills for all the bottom holes that I would be able to reach, this would be around twenty-four in an average Chaside drift. I would then open the det box, bigger than the boxes used in the drifts bored by hand, the reason for this being, the Chaside drifts were much higher and required dets up to a number fifteen, where the lower drifts could be easily fired to the roof with dets up to number twelve. The height of the drifts I had to fire were, at that time, around twenty-two feet, and I would be kept pretty busy during the shift to get the drifts charged. The bottoms were easy enough for me, but climbing up and down the ladder for the top holes took it out of you. I had a variety to fire, not just straightforward drifts, there were flankers, drifts with a canche, sometimes a bench, roofers, the odd pops, these were large blocks of rock, usually the whole cut that had been blown out in one lump, and too large to be loaded. The loaders would put these to one side, the driller would put a hole in on his way past, I would fire them in with the rest of the shots to break them up. There were also the floor shots to fire when required. I liked charging these, they were good to charge: just drop the powder down the holes on top of the primers, and push the dust into the hole after that; the only problem you could get with floor shots was blocked holes, which could take some time to get clear. I did not have to climb up and down a ladder loaded up with powder, and the pile of rock after one good firing would keep the loaders going more than one shift.

At the end of the shift I would be responsible for clearing the area, taking any powder not used back to the reserve station, checking with the lads on hand machines, taking the battery to them to fire, then firing my own shots, when everyone else had set off for the surface. This sounds simple enough and it was, if you knew what you were doing, apart from the odd time when a small loose bit of rock had come off the face after you had charged and tested the drift, and the drift did not fire when you pressed the button. Procedure at that time was to disconnect the firing cable from the battery, take the key out, put it in your pocket, wait ten minutes then go into the

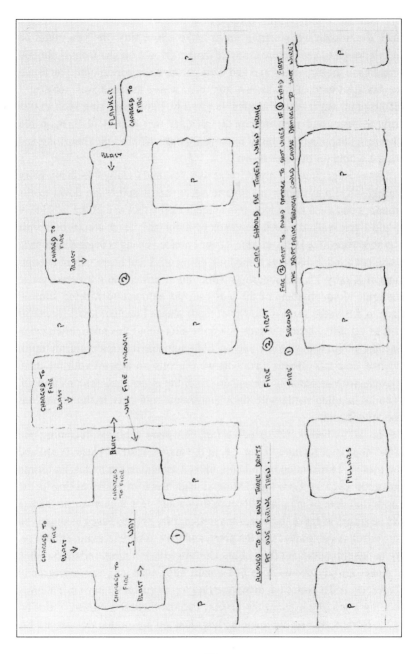

drift and check through the wires on the face. If like me you had always taken the trouble when wiring up to make a nice tidy job, you might be lucky enough to see the broken wire hanging down off the face; if not you would have to start at one end and work through the wiring until you found the damaged wire. If it was in a high drift where the fault was, too bad. I should point out it would happen very rarely, but when firing such as two drifts at once, and then one on its own, or two rounds of three, it did sometimes happen that a bit of rock would drop off after the first firing and bring a whole lot of wires down.

I was just getting into my stride as they say, and I really was in my glory on this job, always busy, no time to spare, but it suited me down to the ground. I had even had a look into another cavity that one of the lads knew of and I had walked past it hundreds of times and never seen it before. It was about this time in my mining career I noticed changes beginning to take place, not a lot, but always something going on. I had heard talk of another mine at Kirkby Thore, Longriggs Mine; up to now I had not been over to this mine although some of the lads had, the entrance to it being situated close to the works itself—another of those places I had not had a chance to visit as yet. I had heard the lads talk quite a lot about this mine, often when discussing bonus payments, one of those subjects that always came up in our bait time talk. Bonus payments were a very sore point with the men, not only with us but with the miners at all the mines, and it seemed to me to be an ongoing battle with the management, not only in the mines, but also at the works.

The works had been expanding fast, this plant was now becoming one of the biggest of its kind in Europe, in the manufacture of plasterboard and bag plaster. I knew men were being moved around in the mines, and some had gone over to Longriggs Mine. I had heard of some asking to be transferred over to the plant, because they could earn higher wages there. I had no desire to leave the mines myself, and we also had men asking to be transferred to the mines from the plant, and they came into mining that way. We in the mines had our three shifts, the Saturday morning, and the Sunday, to make our pay up; we also had a shift allowance and our underground allowance, and a bonus payment on every ton to make our pay up. This was done by a grading system, the drillers had the highest payment, followed by the loaders, and so on down the line. The top pay at that time would be, if the man worked overtime, around £27, the overtime being earned from Saturday morning, Sunday, and by working to four thirty whilst on the six to two shift. Sometimes Saturday or Sunday would be a production shift if extra rock was required by the mill at the plant. This meant extra payments to us being on production, rather than maintenance, one of the conditions brought in at that time by management being, if a man did not put his Sunday in, he would not be asked to work overtime during the week. At one time if a man did not want to work Saturday morning, he could not work the Sunday. These simple minded rules seemed to be made up as we went along. With the requirement for more and more rock, things would have to change, and change they would.

Up to this time Longriggs Mine did not produce a great deal of rock, the bulk of the production coming from the Birks Mine and the Stamphill Mines Well Drift, and the Well Drift was fast coming to an end. At that time I, in my simple way, had not given too much thought to this at all, we just seemed to roll on from week to week, but time was running out and fast. I need not have worried too much, although I didn't know this. The powers above had it all in hand, plans had been drawn up to ensure that young men like me, as I was then just in my prime, as George the foreman would say, would be kept employed for some time to come yet. The Longriggs Mine had only just started to open up, and was said to have a lot of potential. We had discussed this at Birks many times now, mainly picking bits of information up here and there from lads who already worked there. It was said there would be at least sixteen years' work with what reserves of rock were known to be in the ground and already a huge bunker system was in the process of being fired out, using hand machines, by a couple of the best lads from the Well Drift.

Now if a bunker system were being put in, it could only mean one thing: somewhere down the line a tremendous amount of rock would be required to fill it and keep it full, and that would be to keep that plant going flat out—in all a good thing for all of us. Looking back over the years, when the connecting drift had been fired through from the Birks Head Mine into the old Stamphill Mine, just before I had started in 1968, it had been for the very same reason, the requirement for more rock. The way this had been done was to send rock from Birks Mine via the much faster belts system through the connecting drift into a bunker that had been put into the Stamphill

Mine. The extra rock fired with the Chaside drill rig had been loaded by doing away with the old scrapers then in use, and bringing in the front shovel loaders, at the same time doing away with the old aerial ropeway that came overland from Birks Mine Long Marton side. The buckets had a long way to travel across the fields just to get to the Stamphill Mine, the distance from Stamphill Mine to the mill being much less. It had always been hoped to drive a drift through from the Well Drift west into the Longriggs Mine and eventually put belts through, but this would never happen.

Back to Well Drift

I had been told by John, my boss at that time, that I would be going back to the Well Drift, to drill with a hand machine. I was very disappointed to say the least. I had settled down well at Birks and I had my pals there, none of us liked to be moved around too much, but there was little I could do about it. I would be drilling in the old Number One district, drifts that had been left a long time ago, drifts that to me and the lad who would be drilling with me were more like rabbit holes than drifts.

The first shift, I had to bring my machine in and set up ready to drill. What a place, I thought as I marked up the drift, hardly any ventilation. The machines we had to use were known as a Silver Three, a little smaller than the Atlas machines I had used at Birks. The only advantage to me was that they were lighter in weight to handle. After connecting my air hose up and turning on I was ready to begin. I pushed the air control lever forward and made a start on the drift. With the ventilation being so bad, by the time I had bored the cut holes I just had to stop. I could not see the centre mark in the drift three feet in front of my face, it was like standing in a thick fog. I had worked in conditions like this many times before, drilling, but this had to be the worst. I was eating dust. I decided to get my mask from the bait cabin. Not many of the lads would wear a mask, however bad the dust became. I was an exception to that. I would also wear work gloves at times depending on the job I happened to be doing; I had lost enough skin on the vibrator when I first came into mining. Wearing a mask stopped a lot of the dust, the type I used did a good job, but was not the most comfortable thing to wear, and had to be tapped to keep the pad clear after drilling each hole.

I had often been referred to as 'that soft T—— who wears a mask and gloves', and had once been asked by one of the lads why I used a mask. I replied to him, I wore a mask for my benefit, no one else's, if he wanted to eat dust I wouldn't stop him, no one would be the slightest bit bothered. I noticed over the years to come that masks and gloves would be used by almost all the miners, as they became more aware of health and safety in the mines; steel capped boots would be standard, and one pair would be provided by the company once a year.

Roofing back in Wells

After about two weeks drilling in the old Number One district, we had almost exhausted what rock had been left in there, and were told to take our machines out and do some roofing in another part of the mine. The lad I was working with at the time, Collin, had done some roofing before, and knew the drill. I had not, and this would be another experience for me. The place where we would be roofing had already been fired two or three times, and I was very impressed when I saw the piles of rock in the drifts. Collin told me how to set up and left me to get on with it. The first thing I had to do was carry my machine on my shoulder up to the top of the heap. After the second attempt at doing this I decided it would be easier if I took the air hose off first. I could hear Collin's machine going well in his drift, I had put a seven foot drill steel in—we had used six foot in the drifts we had been in—all I had to do was to put six holes in, get them charged and fire them at bait time. We would then drill them again, charge and fire them at the end of shift. I should mention we had to bar down before we could start to drill the roofs, which had of course been fired by the previous shift. The holes in the roof would be put in, one at the top, two in the second row down, three in the row below that. I found I had to take great care while pulling the drill steel back out of the holes while drilling these roofs. The reason for this was that there was a large gap between where I was drilling and the actual heap of fired rock I was standing on to drill off, and if I did not take enough care the drill could fall forward and right down to the bottom of the heap. It was very tiring to lug the machine back up the heap if you let it slip.

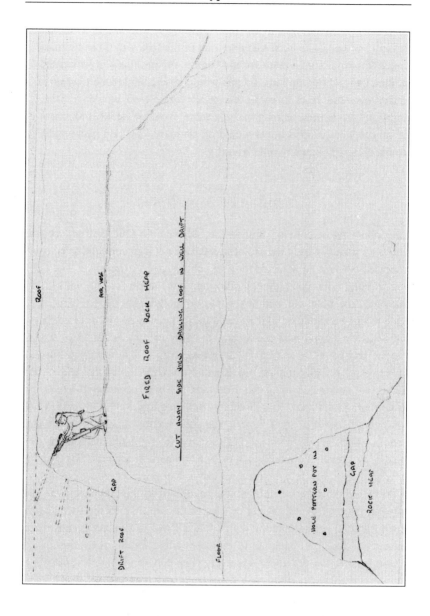

I had worked in the roofing for about a week, when John my boss came to see me in the mine. 'I want you to go to the Longriggs Mine on Monday,' he said. I was a bit stunned, I had become used to being moved around a bit, but to be sent over to Longriggs Mine was like being sent to the end of the world. I asked what the alternatives were if I refused to go. He looked me straight in the eye and replied, 'If you don't go to Longriggs Mine, you will be transferred to the board plant, or sent down the road.' I said in that case I would be at Longriggs Mine on the Monday morning. I was still in a state of shock wondering what I had done to deserve this, but of course it was nothing I had done wrong, it was just the way things were beginning to change at this time, just the start. I had really enjoyed the time I had put in at the Stamphill Mine, and the Birks Mine; I had learned a lot the hard way, but it had been my gain. I would now leave all my mates behind, some I would never see again, some who, although they did not realise it at the time, would soon be following me into the Longriggs Mine.

I felt very sad at the end of my last shift at Stamphill, I had such happy memories of the place: how I had struggled to get to work in clapped out old cars, twenty quid jobs; how I had ridden a motorcycle the twelve miles to the mine in winter, arriving on the early shift unable to speak with the cold—but I had survived, and that to me was the name of the game. While I had worked at Birks Mine I had made many friends, one in particular had turned out to be a great pal and a life long friend.

He had walked over to me at the end of shift one day, as I was waiting to clock off. 'Are you the lad that does the potholing?' he asked. 'I am,' I replied, thinking to myself, another bloke wanting to wind me up about potholing. I was very surprised when asked if I would take him with me on my next trip out. 'Do you really mean that?' I asked him. 'Yes,' he replied, 'I fancy having a go at it.' 'Okay then I will take you down an easy cave not far from here and see how you like it,' I replied, we agreed on a day and that was that.

Pate Hole Cave

I took him to a local cave I liked to visit, a recognised British cave, Pate Hole at a village called Asby. The cave extended to a distance of 1500 feet, classed as a moderate cave and ideal for a first time trip. I noticed as we crawled through a low entrance, a lot more water about than usual, and soon realised it would be a fairly wet trip, but said nothing. I had on my wet suit, I had my share of getting wet and cold in the past, but my companion on this trip, Fred, had only a pair of overalls on, and would soon be put to the test. We quickly found ourselves in water in the canal section of the cave, just up to our knees, there being more water at this point in the cave than I had expected. I knew this cave well and there would be no danger in our going all the way through the system. Fred would not know this, so I stopped and asked him if he wished to continue. I warned him it would get deeper but he wanted to continue.

The water came up to our chests by now but I knew it would get no worse than this, we would soon be out of it at the end of this section of the cave. 'Are you okay?' I asked him. The water was bitterly cold by now, I felt cold myself even with a wet suit on. 'Do you want to go on or have you had enough?' 'Carry on,' he said, again to my surprise, and so we did, all the way through the system, and warmed up in the process.

We had both really enjoyed the trip through the cave, it had been a new experience for my new found friend, and we would in due course of time do some of the finest caving and potholing in Northern England together. What I should mention now after describing that first caving trip with Fred, is the fact that while we were up to our chins, almost, in the bitterly cold cave water, he had not mentioned to me that he was a non-swimmer. I realised, when he told me later, just how determined he must have been to want to carry on through that cave. He was a typical Yorkshireman.

Bunker job

I said cheerio to the lads after my last shift at the mine and presented myself to the foreman at Longriggs Mine on the Monday morning. At that time we had a little bait cabin on the surface, not far from the fan house. I should explain each mine had a fan house on the surface. This was no more than a brick building built on top of the fan shaft, installed into this was the main fan; when this was running, it provided the ventilation for the mine by drawing air up the shaft from the mine workings below.

From the little bait cabin, we would walk down a steep banking that had been cut out in steps, to make this both easier and safer for the men. At the bottom of the steps I stood almost on top of the entrance to the mine, and the road leading into it about twenty feet below. From this point to the road, metal steps had been put in, we had these to descend to reach the road and the entrance to the mine. From here I could see the main plant, no more than four hundred yards away. I could also see the buckets arriving at the mill end to be tipped and sent on their way back to Stamphill Mine. Just then the thought crossed my mind: I had seen hundreds of buckets set off from Stamphill over the past three years, but had never seen where they had arrived till now.

I followed the lads down the steps. The entrance to Longriggs mine would be about seventeen feet or more in height, and a good sixteen feet wide, the roof being flat. When the entrance section had first been driven in from surface, steel girders had been put in and the roof and sides had been concreted. To me, when I first saw it, it seemed enormous after the small half round entrances into Stamphill and Birks, with their half round girders and lagging boards with packing on the top. I looked back up the road from the entrance to the top of the hill. It was about one in eight. The old lorries that had been used to haul the rock out would have had some hassle in winter on ice up here, I thought to myself.

I set off to walk down the mine. It would be the first time I would not be on production since I had started at the mines. The job I would be doing here would be helping to finish off the new bunker system that had been in progress some time now. I found that I had not been the only one to have been sent over from the other two mines: one of the lads, Allan, had come over from Stamphill; he had been on the aerial, sending the buckets of rock over, but had asked to come into the mines, and had come over to Longriggs. Chic, another lad I had met up with before, and old Nels, as we were allowed to call him then. Already things were beginning to look up as they say. We had a small bait cabin down the mine, half way down the road from the mine entrance, we would leave our bait bags, and have our bait here. On the opposite side of the road and a little further down a wooden door in the brattice took you through to the fitting shop and electrician's shop; at this time they were only on a small scale to what they would become in later years. The foreman who would be in charge of us, Johnnie, I had worked

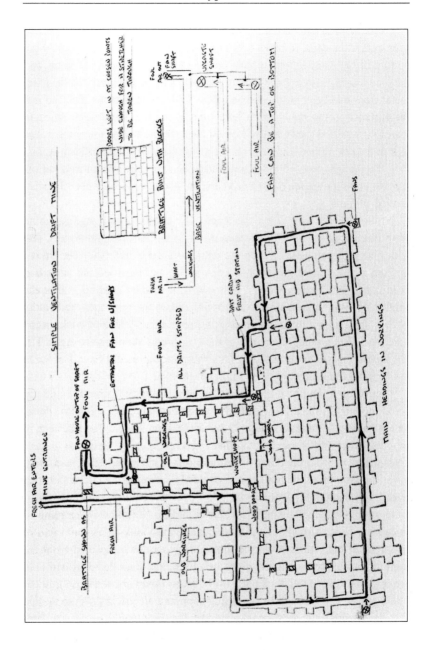

SIMPLE VENTILATION — DRIFT MINE

with before when I had first gone up to the Birks Mine, and I had not realised he had been sent over to this mine some time before.

The job we had to start with first would be to finish off putting in the half round girders. These would eventually form the tunnel that would run from end to end of the bunker when finished. Thousands of tons of rock would be poured in on top of this tunnel when the job was completed; the girders sat on a solid concrete base that had been put down previously, most of the girders had by now been put in, we would put the last ones in. The fitters were having a busy time of it also, as were the electricians working on the job with us. Steel plates had to be welded on top of the girders we had put in, with a hole on one side to allow the rock to drop through. The 'leckys' as they were called had miles of cables to put in, it all looked very complicated, but would all be right in the end.

We had soon put all the steel girders into place, we could get on with the job of putting the shuttering in place ready for the concrete we would have to pour onto the top of all those girders. Looking back over the years, I can really only estimate the length of that tunnel at around one hundred yards total. It was going to be some fun when we came to put the concrete in. We pushed on with putting the shuttering in, this had been specially made up at the joiner's shop for us, due to the shape—a sort of bow shape to fit the girders. There would be about eight of these shutters in total. As they were used and the concrete set, they would be removed and used over again and again until the job had been completed. The concrete used on this job being delivered ready mixed, on the surface, we had a front loader to bring it into the mine for us to use. At first we attempted to shovel it to where it was required on the shuttering. After clearing the first load in this manner it became clear to us that something different would have to be tried if we wished ever to complete the job. All of us on the job had a discussion with the foreman, the outcome of which was that we would use some old belt pans and belting, put the pans along the top of the shuttering, tip the concrete into an old vibrator, not then in use, feed the concrete onto the belt through it. Unlikely though it seemed at the time it actually worked, provided the driver of the mixer lorry put plenty of water in the mix before it was sent down to us on the job. It did have to be assisted through the vibrator with a shovel. The concrete would then come along the belt from the vibrator, we would use a short plank fastened to the pans at the point where

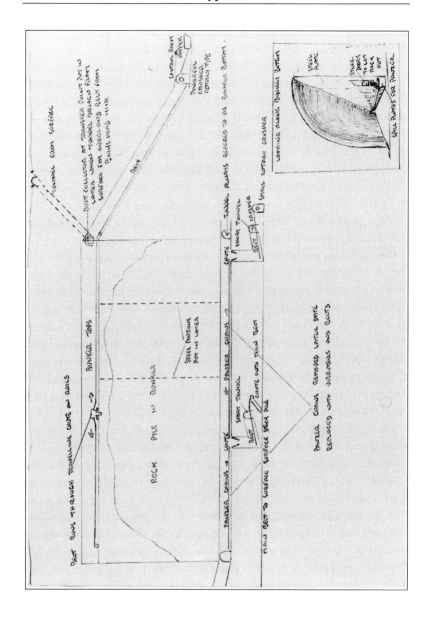

the concrete had to be placed, hold it down across the belt and the concrete poured off it where it was wanted. We completed the job in a very short time in this way, and saved ourselves a lot of shovelling and, most of all, time.

During the time we were employed on the bunker job, contractors were also working in the mine on the same project, putting in the new crusher, the belt structure and belts from the new crusher to the bunker top. This had been a capital investment project by the company in order to increase the output of rock to the level required by the mill for the manufacture of plasterboard and all associated products. The future for us was beginning to look good at last. There would be an awful lot of work to be done yet, to see it all completed, and we had a bit more time to put in on the bunker job yet, before any of us would be on production again. I should at this time mention again, the mine had not yet opened out to its full potential. It had only been opened up a few years previously, and at that time, being in its infancy, was just a very small mine compared to the other two, the main headings only a short distance ahead of the new crusher. The rock from the mine was transported to the surface, from the old crusher then in use, in old tipper lorries, direct to the mill on the surface. When I first came to the mine one of the first things I had noticed had been the absence of belts from the mine. There had been only one belt in the mine at that time, and that had been from the crusher to the loading point for the lorries. The lorries were then in the process of being scrapped, to be replaced with new Muir Hill dump trucks—all part of the capital investment project.

I would spend three months working on the bunker in all. It had been very interesting for me to have been part of, and it all seems a long time ago to me now. One of the jobs we had been involved with at the latter end of my time on this job, had been in putting the panzer chains and pans in. The bottom end of the bunkers had almost been completed by then, almost all the steel work, that is the doors that opened to allow the rock to come out onto the panzer chains. These chains ran the full length of the bunker bottom, they would drop the rock through a small chute onto a short cross belt that in turn would feed onto the main belt. I knew then this would be some mine in the future, if all went well, and looked forward to getting back on to production. I was by this time feeling like a duck out of water. At the same time as we worked on the bunker a whole new section of belts was soon to be put in from the mine all the way to the mill on the surface. The Muir Hill dump trucks would then be used to bring the rock fired in the faces to a hopper with a drag chain in the bottom, to be fed into the crusher, this being a powerful rotary type of foreign manufacture. The crushed rock dropped onto a belt to be taken up the hill to the bunker top, where it could be dropped into the bunker at any point along its length, by means of a travelling chute, the belt carrying the rock running through it. The chute travelled along the top of the bunker on bogey wheels on metal rails. As it reached its further point at either end of the bunker, a wheel would trip a switch, mounted near the rail, and it would stop and then reverse to travel in the opposite direction. The cable controlling the travelling chute being mounted on one side of it on a large reel and, being self winding, it would reel its own cable in as it travelled back along the bunker. It worked very well all the time I was at the mine, but there would have to be a lot done in the future to get the bottom end of the bunker system to run efficiently, and a lot more expense too.

When the bunker had been filled with rock, and we began to run it out of the bottom of the bunker, we had problems with doors jammed with the weight of rock and the amount of rock coming out onto the drag chains. The rock piled up and came over the top of the side plate's overloading the belt taking it away underneath, piling more rock onto the main belt than it could handle. It would take quite a while before it would all be running as intended in the first place, but it did eventually.

I had been told by this time I would be going back onto production again. There had been a lot of changes taking place just now, and men were being moved around. Some of the lads I had worked with at Birks had been sent over to Longriggs Mine by now, and from Stamphill also. We were in the process of gearing ourselves up for a bigger output in production. Those of us who had worked on the bunker job had by this time been told which shifts we were to go on. Rusty, one of the lads who had been on the bunker job with me, had been put on the crusher. He had worked on the aerial at Stamphill before he came to Longriggs, sending the buckets of rock to the mill.

Mine rescue team

Before I had left Stamphill Mine, I had been invited to join the mine rescue team, which I had done along with my drilling partner in the roofing at Stamphill, Collin. We had both started in the rescue team at the same time, and had already put some time in training with the breathing apparatus, under the supervision of Mr Byers, Allan to us. We had of course to be competent in First Aid to be in the rescue team.

I had already gained five certificates in First Aid before I had come into mining, whilst working as an AA patrolman; one of the conditions of employment had been taking lessons in First Aid each year. We would now start taking First Aid as members of the mines rescue team. We had to be competent in the use and maintenance of the breathing equipment we would be using as part of a mine rescue team.

At intervals of about one month we would meet at the rescue station as it was then, at the Stamphill Mine surface, check our breathing apparatus, put it on and wear it for two hours, while walking through the old workings in the mine. While doing this we would check the general condition of the old workings, the state of the roofs, and report any fresh roof falls, and in the process get really used to wearing the breathing apparatus. I always enjoyed these training sessions, even though at times I would feel awfully nauseated with the mouthpiece in for that long.

I had been instructed, when I mentioned it to Allan, that should I actually be sick while wearing the apparatus, I should squeeze the inlet pipe and be sick into the outlet pipe. I can say now I don't think I ever felt that way again.

One of the things I liked about the sessions was that we would always have a mine rescue plan with us, and it was interesting to see all those parts of the mine I never knew existed. On one of the practices, we went into the Birks Mine by way of the old entrance at the Long Marton end; I had been down here before, to the bottom of the workings. I had never gone straight on up the hill into the old white rock area. I was impressed when we walked into the area, just how clean and tidy the place was, the drifts were a treat to see, I could see at once why it was called the white rock area. I had until now only ever seen the gypsum beds I had worked in, with their grey and white beds, this really was white rock, it had been mined with hand machines, and the rock, after firing, had been cleaned out of the drifts using scrapers and brought out in tubs. The roofs in the area were all fired flat and they had been fired out absolutely spot on, all credit to the lads long since gone who had mined that place out. It made our training sessions more interesting coming to parts of the mine like this that I would never have had the chance to see otherwise. Allan had of course been all over the mines at different times in the course of his work, as well as during training sessions in mine rescue, and knew the place like the back of his hand.

One of our training sessions took us into a part of Stamphill I had not seen before. It was close to the old haulage road entrance, and through the brattices on the right hand side, as we walked into the mine from that entrance. The workings were very close to the surface here; Allan took us to where the workings had been so close that when the men had arrived for work the next day, a hole had appeared in the roof. The rock and soil had formed a nice little heap upon the floor of the mine, enabling the men to walk up the heap and into daylight in the field above. All this had happened a few years before.

The story told about this is, when one of the men had contacted the boss outside on the old wind up phone, he informed him there had been a roof fall, with a hole appearing leading into the field above, and as a result half a flock of sheep had got into the mine and were now all over the place. It was said that while the man talked to the boss on the old wind up, the rest of the men had stood around him making superb sheep noises. I have no idea what happened after that, but the story would be repeated to me again on more than one occasion by the older miners. The hole was still there, I could have walked up the heap to daylight if I wished, and it would have been possible for sheep to have got into the mine, at that point quite easily.

I remained a member of the mine rescue team for around four years, before I gave it up. By this time I was involved in other things, and had very little time to spare, I was putting a lot of time in exploring old lead mines in the area, with my mate Fred, the old mines being fitted in between our potholing trips to the Easegill cave systems. We were both members of the Red Rose cave and potholing club and there were those, of course, who just could not understand why we found pleasure in potholing, being miners in the first place. For the pair of us this would be an ongoing argument for a very long time, but we had a lot of fun winding up the people who were all against this kind of activity. I should mention at this time, on our frequent visits to the potholing club we encountered a lot of opposition to our visits to old mines from the hard core potholing fraternity. It was very understandable, after all the club was what it declared itself to be, a cave and potholing club.

To raise cash for the benefit of the said club, we occasionally held a club auction. It was to one such auction I took a selection of choice pieces of daisy bed, and some pieces of highly collectable selenite Fred and I had, along with fluorspar, and rock crystal. The auctions always attracted a gathering of the members in support of their club, and when our little collection of rocks came under hammer, the prices bid for them were exceptionally high, to our amazement. From then on we were rather popular around the place, and members took a great deal more interest in mines than they had previously, so much so visits to our area were arranged. However, in the meanwhile we were having to earn a living and, as Fred had also been sent over to Longriggs, we were now able to plan our little camping expeditions better, and visit many more mines in the area.

The number of men moved into the mine had been for a purpose, this being the extraction of a lot more rock for the large board plant that had by this time been constructed on the surface. We would still work three shifts but with a lot more men in them than there had previously been. It is worth mentioning that the drilling machines here were Secoma drill rigs, mounted on Marshall tractors. They were mounted on tracks, but had a good turn of speed and were capable of putting holes into the faces at speed with their twin booms. They could travel around the mine as it was then in a very short time, drilling holes into any drift that happened to be empty, and were always way ahead of the chargers and loaders. The men would organise themselves with regard to the work to be done, the drillers with the barring down, charging, and the drilling, the loaders with the loading, and transporting of rock to the tipping point at the crusher hopper. At first the lads I worked with would all bar down together, then we would charge all the drifts required together, one man on the drill rig for a week at a time changing around. Some of the men preferred not to take their turn on the rig, being quite happy to bar down and charge. We had by this time acquired from one of the ICI mines over the North East some second hand equipment, one of the machines that came to us being an old Chaside tractor, which had been used with a bucket fitted to load rock. Our fitters put a platform onto this machine, and converted it into a scaler cum mobile charging platform, something we really had been in need of for some time.

The tonnage by now had been increasing all the time. It would be only natural for the men to seek a change in bonus payments. It would also be expected the company would seek to keep these payments to a minimum, in order to recoup some of the capital expenditure it had invested in the mine. We were all union members, not of the NUM, as some might have thought, but members of the the GMWU. This union had been one of those the company had agreed to negotiate with long before I had come to the mines. On my very first day at the mines I had been asked to join the union, and I had accepted. There were some who never did join a union, but the choice was theirs to be made.

It would not take us too long to organise ourselves with regard to the work that had to be done to reach to tonnage targets, set out by management in our bonus agreements with the union. We soon came up with a system of work suitable to all involved, but each shift acted on its own initiative as to how it would be done. The lads on my shift would have a change around on the drill rig each week. Two men would scale all the tops of the drifts using the Chaside scaler, one man would scale all the drift bottoms. When this work had been completed all three men would then set to, and do the charging between them; two men would be responsible for charging the bottom half of the drifts, and one man would charge all the roofs, using the Chaside scaler. I would think we were charging around six or more drifts on a shift, at that time, after we had finished the scaling work. The scaling down of the drifts could take a lot of time, depending on how roughly the drifts had been fired, and sometimes very little time at all. It was just one of those jobs that could not possibly have a time fixed, it would have been very irresponsible of anyone to do that. Safety would have to come before tons, and this was a rule I would always stick to, all the time I worked at the mines.

With all the different lads jumping on the drill rig at this time and, in some instances, to learn the job, it was no wonder the barring down or scaling was so bad and took so long sometimes to complete. There would be many complaints about the condition of the drifts after they had been fired, and also after they had been scaled. I heard the shout many times, 'Hast thou pillocks bin using baking powder to fire wid er wat?'

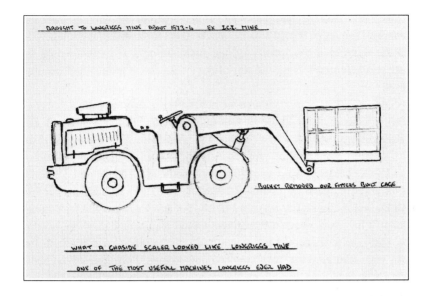

BROUGHT TO LONGRIGGS MINE ABOUT 1973-4   EX I.C.I. MINE

BUCKET REMOVED OUR FITTERS BUILT CAGE

WHAT A GHASIDE SCALER LOOKED LIKE LONGRIGGS MINE

ONE OF THE MOST USEFULL MACHINES LONGRIGGS EVER HAD

Something would have to be sorted out and fast. First of all we would have only one man on the drill rig, and he would do all of the drilling, all of the time. Those of us who were quite capable of standing in for that man if necessary, would do so as and when required, those who were not would keep off the drill rig; all the three shifts would work the same system. The loaders had their own system for doing their work at this time, I believe they would take turn about on the shovel loader loading the Muir Hill dump trucks hauling the rock to the crusher, either day about or week about, I can't be sure. This system would be in use almost all the time I worked at Longriggs Mine with very slight variations to it.

Production would increase slowly but surely as the months passed, to meet the ever increasing demands of the plant. Up to now the bulk of the rock had been mined from the main heading, and from an area to the west of it known to us as the banks. A small area at the back of the bunker had almost been worked out by this time, and because of a fault would have to be stopped. Water had also become a nuisance near the crusher and a small pump had been installed. The main heading would soon come to a stop; it had been mined on a slope of about one in eight with the dip to the east, the workings on that side of the main heading had all come to a stop due

93

to the same fault we had met with on that side, all the way up from the crusher. Production would now be concentrated in an area to the south-west of the mine, and the quality of the rock during this period would be exceptionally good; from the top of the banks the workings had become level.

Only one thing spoilt this area we now worked, the road to the crusher— okay on the level for the Muir Hill dump trucks, but that last run to the crusher down the road at the banks really was steep. With a heavy load on the trailer it was definitely not for the faint hearted; I would find that out for myself because of the ever increasing demand for more rock. We had been asked if we would work through our bait time to keep production going, that is those of us who had tickets for driving diesel vehicles in the mine. It had been decided the drivers would take their bait at the normal bait time, two of the shotfirers would do the loading and haulage to the crusher whilst they had their twenty-minute break. I was one of the shot-firers who would do this having had previous experience at loading. H, one of the loaders, would give me a little tuition on the Muir Hill dump truck, this being one trip to the crusher with him riding on the Muir Hill after I had loaded it. At the top of the hill on the banks, I asked what gear did they use normally to negotiate the hill, bearing in mind the trailer was separate from the tractor pulling it. 'High five,' came the reply. Too late, I had put it into that gear and we were on our way. Thankfully I kept my head, concentrated on keeping the tractor in a straight line and the trailer brake worked when H had hit it. At the bottom of the hill H looked at me and said, 'I was only kidding, you mad sod.' I can't put down on paper what I said at the time, I had been lucky. A short time after that one of the tractors had the front end smashed off on the same hill after it had jack-knifed, with no one injured.

It would not be long now before the old Muir Hill tractors would be replaced with Volvo dump trucks to meet the demand for more production, the shovel loaders were already being replaced with new Terex loaders, this being an articulated vehicle, with a much bigger bucket on the front and more powerful than we had used previously. Loading through bait time had not been a good idea in the first place and had to be scrapped, the amount of rock loaded did not justify the hammer the machines had to take with different inexperienced drivers jumping on and off them, that goes for any machine. In the meantime the two Secoma drill rigs were destined to last us a very long time, they were still in service when I left Longriggs mine years later.

We were now entering about the best period in the life of the mine, because of the demand for more production—12,000 to 14,000 tons weekly—the miners resolved to meet this with a willingness I had not seen before. The drifts we were now firing were on average around twenty feet and more high, with a hundred ton plus on a round after each firing, keeping us well in advance of the loaders. The scaling down being at times just plain hellish.

By this time we had a new mines manager, we had also had a new washroom cum bait cabin built at the bottom of the hill from the mine entrance with a mine store built at the back of it. In the new bait cabin we had tables and benches made for us by the mine's joiner, the wash-hand basins with hot water being a real luxury to us. The workshops had been expanded to cope with all the new machines that had to be serviced and repaired, I should point out the old bait cabins were still used by those of us working too far away to reach the new bait cabin until end of shift, when we would gather to get washed up.

On top of the banks it had been decided to mine under what on the surface had been a peat bog or so I was told. It would be in the same direction as the main heading had been taking; this area would be known to the lads as the lakes, due to the fact it had plenty of water in it. We were now getting a lot further away from the crusher, and a decision had been made to put a haulage belt in to the crusher, this belt would have a vibrator on the end to feed rock onto it. The vibrator had been one of those salvaged from the Stamphill Mine, along with anything else that could be salvaged from that mine. Very shortly after I had left Stamphill Mine, the rest of the men employed there had been moved to either Birks Mine or Longriggs Mine, transferred to the plasterboard factory, or had left. The few men remaining had been engaged on salvage work as far as I know. I had been left for some time now and had lost touch with the place.

Cave-in at Stamphill

Stamphill Mine had caved in one Sunday morning, part of the Well Drift had gone the following Sunday when some more had collapsed. Myself and about six others had been sent over to Stamphill Mine to assist with some salvage work, on the Sunday morning following the last cave-in, it would be the last salvage operation before being bricked up I was told. We had been delayed getting over to the mine waiting for transport. After waiting some considerable time we decided it was bait time. Eventually the transport arrived and took us to Stamphill Mine. Myself and the rest of the lads had collected lamps at the mine lamp house and were waiting instructions at the lamp house, this being situated two or three yards from the mine entrance. At around 10 a.m. I was suddenly aware of a terrific noise that became louder and louder as we stood there, followed by a rumbling noise—suddenly the whole area in front of us became filled with dust and chippings flying about everywhere, it was like a thick white fog. By this time the sound I had at first heard had become a loud screaming noise. I stepped out of the lamp house to find out what was happening, and I could see dust and chippings pouring out of the mine entrance in front of me. Just then Allan, the lad who had brought us in the Landrover, came to us, 'It's been a big one this time, lads,' he said. 'The whole mine has gone.' When I asked about the screaming noise he told me it was the main fan; it had been forced to run in reverse, the bearings must be red hot by now.

After all the dust had settled down and we began to take in what had happened, we realised just how lucky we had been on that day. True enough the whole of the Well Drift had caved in. It was said later that the pillars had sunk through the floor, thirteen acres of surface had sunk up to fifteen feet. Only two men had been working in the mine at the time so I was informed later, they had been belt cleaning up the nine belt connecting drift, they were badly shaken by it all but mercifully uninjured. The two men, young Kenny and old Johnty, had been lucky, they had been away up the connecting drift at the time, but it had been very frightening for the pair of them all the same.

The belt we put in to the crusher would only be from the top of the banks at that time, and would be a rope belt; up to this time I had not seen a rope belt. After a hole had been fired through the pillar side a bridge had to be

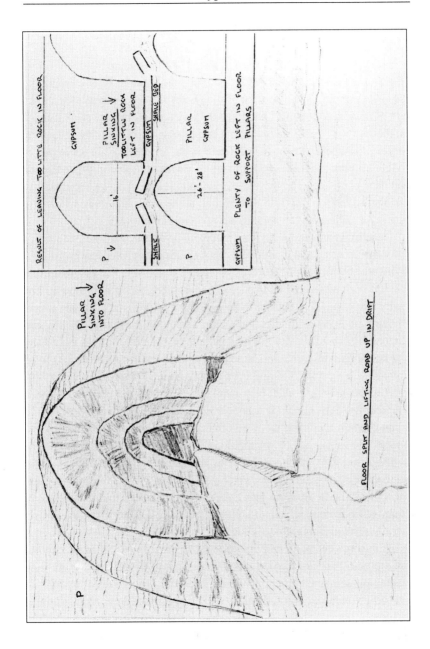

built across the road to take the belt over the hopper at the crusher to allow rock to drop into it. When this work had been completed the rope belt could be put in. I would not be involved in this, it had been done by the two other shifts on their maintenance days. I had only assisted the fitter with putting the gear head into place and with drilling holes that would be used to anchor it in place with roof bolts. I had liked the way the rollers were all suspended on the two very heavy main cables, these being supported throughout the length of the belt with metal supports; if one or other of the main cables should become damaged the whole set up would come down. When the belt had been completed and the vibrator put on the end of it, we soon put it to use sending rock along it to the crusher, at the same time rock would still be hauled to the crusher with the new Volvo dump trucks.

The area we now mined had a number of cavities in the floor, we seemed to hit new ones almost every shift; these cavities were very low and dry, or at the worst with very little water. We had found one in the side of a pillar that had been exposed after firing and had left long pillars at this point. The cavity was exposed in the side of the pillar after firing two drifts further on. At that time I was drilling in a corner at a point where the rope belt would come to the top of the hill. I put a test hole into the floor on the right hand side of the drift, after the steel had sunk into the rock about one foot it jerked forward into a cavity; I allowed the steel to slide all the way in to see how far it would travel, it went in the full length. I reported it to the foreman who came to take a look; it was decided to fire one of the holes closest to it and fire it at bait time, we would then get a better look at the cavity, and a better idea of its size. It was fired and a nice clean hole knocked into the cavity, it would be no more than four foot six in height but it went on for some distance as far as we could see with our cap lamps. What water there was in it would be no more than a foot deep. I had been told to keep out of it, and after seeing the size of some of the slabs hanging from the roof in there I, decided it might be a good idea.

After some checking had been done, this cavity I had hit was found to link up with the ones already mentioned exposed in the sides of the long pillars, the combined length of the cavities being about five or six pillars. The drift would not be fired again, rock being tipped in to block the hole and is still there to this day, should anyone care to look.

By this time our present heading was toward the north-west, held on that course due to a fault on the west side of that heading. At the same time we would be breaking new ground on the north-east side going around the back of the fitting shop, all the haulage in that area being done with the Volvo dumpers. The main heading had by this time been stopped and work under the peat bog also, a decision had been taken what to do about the bunker bottom. A lot of money would have to be found to put the bunker bottom to rights, and somehow it must have been found. The system I had helped to put in when I first came to Longriggs Mine had probably seemed like a good idea at the time but it just did not function as well as had been expected. The drag chains or panzer as it was called did the job it had been put in to do: drag the rock that came out of the bottom of the bunker to the chute that dropped it onto a belt, the problem being to get the rock out of the bunker bottom in the first place. The steel slide doors supposed to let the rock out onto the panzer would stick or would open too wide, or not open enough, the rock above would stick and not drop out, or drop with a rush all over the place. Just about everything had been tried to make the system work, in sheer desperation I would think, remembering the whole thing would be about one hundred yards in length, and about forty feet high to where the rock would be tipped into the bunker top off the belt. The poor lad on the bunker bottom would have to bray the doors, and steel plates to try to get the rock to drop, which it did with a mighty rush. Sometimes he would be desperate enough to shove a long steel bar up through the door, and this was highly dangerous.

Eventually the brains were brought in to sort the job out. They gave it a lot of thought, and came up with the brilliant idea of using a belt to run the whole length of the bunker. It would be placed underneath the openings for the rock, rather than to one side as the panzer had been installed. Best of all where the rock dropped out of the bunker, a vibrator would be put in to encourage the rock to drop onto the belt. We had used this system of vibrators in the bunkers at Stamphill Mine years before, and for that matter were still feeding rock onto the belts in the north-west side of the mine at that time, through vibrators that had been used in Stamphill Mine. It would take a lot of hard work and time to make the conversion, and I would not even attempt to put a figure on the cost involved; but what a good system when it had been completed, it would run with very little trouble.

Another point while on the subject of the bunker: when it had first been put in or rather fired out, it had been fired down to the floor level in the drifts below. I have already said previously when I came to the mine to work on the bunker, this floor had been concreted over and a good job done. The steel arch girders had then been put in place, they had been covered in concrete; rock had then been fed into the bunker over the tunnel we had built in the bottom, and hopefully it would find its way through the openings left in the bottom onto the panzer to take it away. This resulted in thousands of tons of rock remaining in the bunker unable to get out, because it was settled on a flat base, and would not shift from there unless moved, as it eventually had to be for the conversion, with a shovel loader. The miners had talked about this at bait times when the bunker had reached the girder stage, having expected steel plates to be placed over the girders, and at such an angle as to allow the rock to feed itself into the openings we had left, although it would have reduced the overall capacity of the bunker. It had been expected when the conversion to belts and vibrators had taken place, this might have been given some thought at the time. it never was, and perhaps for a very good reason, I don't know. Later on during a holiday period for which I had permission to work, I would be assisting contractors, with my old mate Fred, in the erection of a steel partition to keep the rock separate in the bunker. One had already been put in, which I had not been involved with. After Stamphill Mine had caved in and the surface buildings had all been removed, and the old aerial ropeway had been taken away, a large amount of capital would have to be invested in the old Birks Head Mine.

I feel I should remind the reader that the period I am writing about covers twenty-four years, from September 1968 to November 1992. I am attempting to put to paper, no more and no less than my own memories and experience, as a gypsum miner, and the mines I worked in. I will write what I can about the Birks Head Mine, and that is very little, due to the fact I worked there in 1971, before being sent over to Longriggs Mine, and had not been back there for a considerable number of years, and as we say had lost touch.

Birks Head Mine was not too far along the road from the village of Long Marton, as I had already stated and a large amount of capital would have to be invested in this mine. It would have to be, if the mines were to produce the amount of rock required to keep the new automated plant at Kirkby

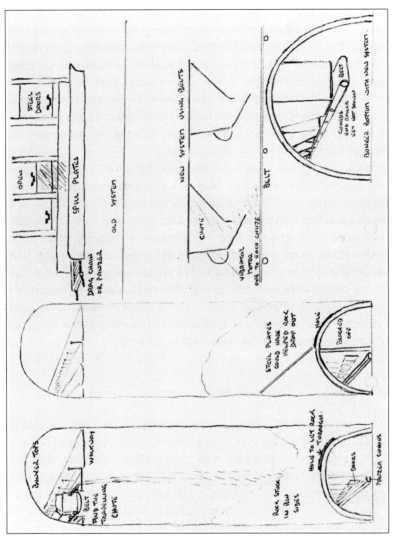

Thore producing plaster board. At this time Longriggs Mine produced the
bulk of the rock being used in the plant, and would continue to do so until
major work had been completed at Birks Head Mine. The work included
the driving of a new main adit into the mine at a point close to the Long
Marton road, and this work would take some time before it would be

completed. A new underground bunker would have to be installed, along with the crusher, a drift would be driven underground, underneath the Long Marton road, to surface in a field from where a new overland conveyor belt would take all the rock produced in the mine to the bunker in Longriggs Mine. Contractors were employed to drive a tunnel from the surface down to the bunker in Longriggs Mine, this tunnel would be supported with arch girders and lagged from surface to bunker. While this work was in progress, Birks Head Mine itself would be developed in a big way, using new drill rigs and front loaders.

Back at Longriggs Mine we were going flat out to produce the extra tonnage, and I believe at one stage we produced upwards of fourteen thousand tons a week. We at Longriggs would continue to send the bulk of the rock required to meet the demands of the plant, until such time as Birks Head Mine could send rock over to our bunker in Longriggs Mine via the overland belt. At the same time as Birks Head Mine was being opened up and developed it would become a highly mechanised mine, with the intro-duction of new GHH front loaders with their huge buckets for loading, and new drill rigs. At Longriggs Mine, for us it would be much of the same, production six days a week, on three shifts, and it began to show it was now becoming a monotonous slog from shift to shift.

The Accident

The mines at Kirkby Thore did at this time have an almost clear record for accidents, but we did have one. I well remember, it happened just before or about the time we finished work in the main heading. Dolly, one of the lads, and myself had been roof bolting in the main heading, using the Hudson scaling carriage, the drift we were in had only a low roof, but we had put a number of roof bolts in. After our shift had clocked off and gone home, two lads on the incoming shift had taken over bolting where Dolly and I had left off. When we clocked on at 0600 the following morning we heard there had been an accident, two of the lads had been injured, one seriously, while roof bolting.

The accident had occurred when the cage with the two lads in it had apparently snapped off at a welded joint on part of the boom, and this part had the cage they were working in attached to it. The cage had then tipped forward in an instant, throwing the lads in it to the front of the cage just before hitting the floor, the heavy stoping machine falling onto one of them causing his injury.

The accident came as quite a shock to us all at that time, the Hudson had been taken out of service until the investigation had been completed, it would then be modified to new specifications. I believe it was at this time that a new Hudson scaling carriage built to new specification was brought into the mine.

By now the mine was being opened up, the north-west workings would not last much longer due to faults and water problems, although we did not know this. The belt in that district had been extended for some considerable distance, a bridge had been built over it for access, and floor would be fired out at selected places. We had some water here but nothing serious. What water we had encountered up to now had all been piped to the main wells, close to the bunker from where it could be pumped to the surface. The fault running with us on the west side of this area prevented us breaking through as we would have liked, forcing us to continue the driving back towards the main office block and the plant. On the north-east side of the mine, in an area at the back of the bunker, we found ourselves in amongst the water and another fault. I mentioned earlier a cavity found in this area where a pump had to be installed due to the amount of water it was making. Because of the water and faults, we would have to turn north and drive along the back of the fitting shop.

About this time the Birks Head Mine started sending its rock over to our bunker through the overland belt system, the talk of the mines being that Birks would be the daddy of all the mines at Kirkby Thore now it was into gear.

I also remember very well some of the great characters we had in the mines at this time, and feel I should mention just some of the nicknames they had been given. Old Moor, ex-lead and barytes miner, worked at the Silverband Mine up on Dunfell. Along with Big Jeff, Rupe, Big Geordie, they had come to the gypsum mines with others when The Band, as it was known as locally, had closed. You had to be careful or you soon had a handle attached to your name, I had at one time been called Rocky, by H, but luckily for me it had not caught on. We had Dusty, for obvious reasons,

Dabber, Wild Bill, sometimes plain Big Bill, Topper, one of the young bucks in the fitting shop called Dog, Bernard almost always known as Marrer. One unfortunate lad had to put up with being called Nutty, I have no idea why. It had always been the custom in the mines to call a man by his christian name, even if it happened to be the boss. He in turn would always call a man by his christian name, and you could be sure of one thing, if he were not too sure of a man's name, he would ask the under-manager or foreman before he spoke to him.

It was while we were firing those drifts down past the back of the fitting shop that some more selenite was exposed after one firing, quite a tidy little deposit. Unfortunately most of it would be shattered on firing, but we did save a few pieces before the loaders took it all to the crusher. As I have already said we were unable to break new ground on the east side in these drifts due to a fault and also water. We had been lucky enough not to have too many chlorides in our rock, and at the same time we had mined almost exclusively in very good quality rock, which I suspect had spoiled us. I had by this time packed in the mine rescue and First Aid, after a period of about five years. I think the reason for this at the time was that Allan who had been in charge up to that time, had also given it up, and Collin had left the mine to got into business as a newsagent. Over on the north-west side, by now it had been driven for some considerable distance, the heading would fast be coming to a full stop, although some workings had been opened up on the east side of the heading. By this time we had come past the new bait cabin and mines store, to which had been added an underground laboratory there for the purpose of testing rock samples, situated at the bottom of the hill close to the main adit. A road had been fired down at one in eight to meet the road at the bottom of the main adit, while work in the heading on the north-west side had almost come to a stop, water being the problem. It was a disappointment to us as we had expected to mine much further than this.

Into one of the drifts in the heading tons of concrete had been poured, roof bolts had been put into the floor and when the concrete had set plates were put on the roof bolts and tightened down with nuts. It held for only a very short while before the concrete began to lift, a pump would be installed to pump the water away to the wells and we would concentrate on the north-east heading.

Drifts below the railway

Two men had been employed on development work on the north-east side for some time now. The company had obtained permission to drive two drifts at one in eight to the east; the two drifts would take us below the main railway line. They had been driven through what to us had been no more than rubbish, all the rock fired had to be dumped in back drifts to get rid of it. Hand machines had been used on this development at first, this had been too slow, something would have to be done to speed the work up. The two Secoma rigs could not be taken off production, for any reason. It was decided to bring in an old drill rig from one of the other mines, Newbiggin Mine. The rig itself was really no more that an old Fordson tractor with two booms mounted on the back end. The drill machines were in fact two Silver Three machines and very noisy when the pair of them were going at the same time, the rock in the development being very hard compared to the softer gypsum rock, made them cough a bit. It would not be long before the first cut through would be made, and a tidy little area opened up into rock of the quality we required, at this time I would be working in the north-east heading.

While working in this heading, Fred and I found some very lovely gypsum crystals or selenite. We had found water in this heading and it really was a pain, we all knew it would soon be stopped. A very small cavity had been fired into, it had been full of water, I stood looking into the water which had by this time cleared, I could see it was obviously continuing to seep in and this would need to be pumped away. I took a closer look at the water, I could see lots of crystals on the bottom, very small but really lovely. The water being no more than a foot I reached in and lifted them out. We would mine a bit more rock out in this heading before it was stopped sooner than we had expected to, and this had been a good thing for us. It had allowed time for the two drifts being driven under the railway to be pushed well on. The small area being opened up at the cut through had been getting larger with every shift, and the heading in here would be to the north-east again.

On the other side of the mine, the north-west heading had come to a stop, a small area had been mined out to the east side of the heading. It had always been hoped this area would have linked up with the heading we had been driving on the north-east side all this time, in fact it was only a matter of yards separating the two sets of workings. To supplement production flooring had been fired out at selected parts of the mine, and this had all been of high quality rock with low chlorides in it. The Birks Mine had been sending rock over for some time now, not too much at first but it would now be The Mine, as the lads would say. And it would indeed be The Mine, it was now highly mechanised, all new machines had been purchased to do it, we were beginning to feel like the poor relative. The one advantage we had over them was that we had low salts in our rock, although by this time the percentage of gypsum in our rock would be lower than it had been previously but it was still good rock.

A number of changes would shortly take place, one of the most important for me being that, after our shop steward had resigned, I had been proposed and seconded by the lads to become their shop steward at Longriggs mine. I took up my duties in April 1978. this had been a challenge to me which I had been unable to resist. After ten years in the mines I felt I had enough experience to be able to speak up on behalf of the men I would be representing, and in the following years I would do just that.

Our pets

I feel now might be a good time to mention our pets, and by pets I don't mean the rats and mice, which we had by now almost eliminated, thanks to the splendid efforts of the pest control man from a well known company. The pets I want to mention, guests might be a better way of describing them, and I mention them only as a matter of interest. Firstly the bats, I can't say what sort, I don't know, to me a bat is a bat. We would see them flying up and down the main adit from the entrance to the bait cabin at the bottom of the hill, on occasions even further. I never saw them in any part of the mine other than the main adit, the small area of workings at the bottom of the hill, and along the road as far as the wells.

Along the road from the bottom of the main adit a small crusher had been put in over the main belt, it could be fed with rock off a short cross belt from the bunker. Walking past this early one morning, I saw an outline on the top of the crusher. As I walked closer I saw an owl, it amused me the way its head pivoted around on its body to watch me as I walked past. I mentioned the owl to the lads at bait, they said. 'Sometimes never see it for weeks, then it comes back again.'

We also had our robin. This cheeky little bird appeared in the winter months and would find it's way down to the bait cabin at the bottom of the adit. The robin would sit on the table in the cabin happy as a king and so it should be, it would get as much attention as a king.

During periods of heavy rain on the surface, a lot of water washed down the road from the new office and changing rooms at the top of the hill to the mine entrance; it would pour through the six inch steel pipes put there to drain it away to the bottom of the hill in the main adit. The water came through a cut through at the bottom of the hill into old workings used as a catchment for it, from there it drained through pipes to the wells. We found small frogs in here, and at times would gather some and take them out of the mine at the end of shift. One of the fitters who shall remain nameless found a large dead toad, it had been dead for some time by the look of it. He waited until Dabber, one of the lads was about to rinse his face whilst having a wash, and popped it into the water. Dabber almost jumped two feet in the air as he looked to see what he was holding in his hands, much to the amusement of those present at the time. A short time later the same fitter was not amused when he came in for his bait to find his pint pot super-glued to the bench and the lid of his bait box likewise.

We also had a stray cat, a very young cat which followed the lads to the bait cabin one day; it looked half starved. We thought would be unfair to keep the cat in the mine because it may well have been injured, so it was stuffed full with best sandwiches and taken home for a pet by one of the lads. I think it would be a while after, when it was reported to the under-manager Wilf, that a cat had been seen in the bunker by the bunker man; it was thought to be dead as it had not moved. When the under-manager came to take a look, because of the danger involved in entering the bunker system and because it looked to be dead, it was decided to leave it where it was. The following day by a sheer stroke of good fortune, the belt patrolman, on the surface at that time, saw the cat as it travelled up the belt in amongst the rock, and pulled it off. The cat was then taken to the office where it was found to be alive, placed in a box, by one of the lads given milk and food, and cleaned. Although it was half starved, it was not known how long it may have been trapped in the bunker, it showed no sign of any injury, and recovered within days, When the office door was left open it was seen to take off across the adjacent fields, like a rocket, according to one of the lads. We could not believe how lucky that cat had been. It was thought that what had happened was this: the cat had somehow managed to get onto the overland belt system, the belt coming over to Longriggs Mine bunker from Birks Head Mine. Because this belt system is covered in, it may have been unable to get out so it would be tipped into the bunker system in Longriggs Mine, only after passing over the transfer points, whilst on the belt. Then through the dust collection unit, and onto the belt in the top of the bunker, from there through a steel chute into the bunker, dropping perhaps twenty feet or more, but with some luck, the point at which it dropped into the bunker, may have been almost full and it might have dropped no more than seven foot. Even more amazing was how it survived without being crushed to death in the bunker, with hundreds of tons of rock pouring in on top of it, and then to be dragged with the rock through the vibrator in the bottom of the bunker, onto the belt that would drop it through a steel chute onto another belt, through yet another steel chute onto the belt taking it to the surface. I heard one of the lads say at the time, that poor cat has used all its lives up by now surely, but what pleased us the most, being the fact that the poor thing had survived and seemingly none the worse for its experience.

I had settled down very well to my duties as one of the mine's shop stewards; it had taken me some time to get used to being fired at from both sides but I seemed to enjoy this, it gave me a lot to think about. In the nine years I would eventually spend as shop steward, I don't think I could ever have been called militant – ruthless yes, but never militant. This particular year had been quite an eventful one for me in some respects, I had become a shop steward for one thing, and I had also made my very first parachute jump at Kirkbride near Carlisle, at the age of forty-one. Potholing had dropped off a little by now, and my visits to the club became less, and this did please my long suffering wife, but she would have to put up with my parachuting for some time.

Meetings with management had become frequent due to negotiations with them over bonus payments, and I would enjoy some memorable battles if I may call them battles, on the subject of bonus payments. I would also have many minor skirmishes with management on the subject of health and safety, which at this time had been tightened up in most work places in the country.

By now Longriggs Mine had been put onto two shifts only. This at first had not been a popular move because of the loss of the three shift pay, after we had been on two shifts for a little while, three shift payments would soon be forgotten. With the mighty Birks Mine, able if it wished to pump rock via the overland belt at an alarming rate into our bunker, some of the lads had already been transferred to that mine from Longriggs besides the new men now employed at that mine. We at Longriggs Mine had been busy, and had opened up on the other side of the railway lines, the two drifts had been taken down at one in eight, and we were now loading rock out of two small areas, one being about half way down with a heading to the north-east, one at the bottom of the hill also to the north-east. At this time the reek off the Volvo dumpers hauling the rock to the crusher was very unpleasant to all of us working in that place, especially when they were pulling hard to get up the one in eight.

A new bait cabin had been built for us at the top of the hill with tables and benches, made for us by the joiner, the bricklayer had also been kept fully occupied building stoppings all over the mine for some time now. The workings at the bottom of the two one in eight drifts had levelled off and were now level, the headings in the area being to the north-east. We would also drive drifts to the east side, later on to the west, no attempt being made to drive drifts to the south. When the two one in eight drifts had been driven about half the distance down, from the top to the bottom, we had at that time taken a drift to the south, but after some distance had come to a stop. During the time I worked in there we never tried to mine on that side again, I don't know just what the problem had been, but it was nothing to do with water that stopped us. We had high hopes for this area we had now started to mine, because at this time we had nowhere else to go, that's how it is with any mining operation, mine it out and move on. The two shifts as we now were, worked in the same way, one man on the drill rig all the time, someone would stand in for him, should he be off; two men charging, two men scaling the roofs of the drifts; one man doing all the bottoms, these lads would change around at the end of the week, it was hard work and very monotonous. The lads on the loading side had their own system of working, it was one long drag to the crusher and back on a round trip, even with the Volvo dumpers, from the headings we were now working.

I believe at this time I was involved in some pretty tough negotiating, with management, dealing with our bonus payments as usual. I might add, our basic pay at that time was the same as the lowest agricultural rate of pay. After one meeting to attempt to sort out the bonus payments, when in general conversation with one of the junior managers in the plant on the surface, he turned to me and said, 'You're not miners down there, they are just quarries with a lid on.'

I resolved from that day to be even more ruthless, and I was.

I thought to myself at the time, what would a wanker like that know about mining, his total experience of mining gypsum can't have been any more than a quick flip around one of the company mines in a Landrover.

From time to time we did have young men, just out of university working with us, being trained on all the jobs in the mine and working alongside the lads. They worked the same shift as we did. They received no favours, not from management or miners, and no doubt at times they would collect a good bulling from some of the lads. If, after a period of time, they proved to be made of the right stuff, they would have earned the right to be given the opportunity to climb the company ladder and go on to better themselves. I could name at least two who did go on to become managers at other mines in the company.

In the meantime we had no choice but to get on with the job in hand to the best of our ability. The bonus negotiations had not reached a conclusion, time and motion men had been brought in, about six of them to do the business on the loaders, with our blessing I might add. The distance from the workings to the crusher, had by this time become a very long round trip, to us it had become pretty obvious something would have to be done and soon. We were in fact waiting for the new belt system to be finished, and until this had been done, what would be the point in us negotiating a new bonus scheme.

During the time we had been having meetings to work out a bonus based on the running times of the Volvo dumpers, as I have already said, a new system of belts had been planned out and was in the process of being put in, brand new belt structure and all. Whilst the time and motion men had been in the mine, timing the Volvo dumpers, work on the new belt had progressed almost as far as the two drifts that had been driven under the railway, and would be no more than a few weeks away from completion or near enough. Once the belt had been completed and running then we could get down to negotiating a new bonus scheme based only on tonnages going up that belt. The finished belt would run all the way from the north-east side up the one in eight return airway drift under the railway, to the top of the hill; from there it would go across to the old north-west workings, which had already been fired through for that purpose, and on to meet the system already in the north-west workings, a considerable distance, all the way to the crusher. What we being simple miners could not understand, (and we would have had to be blind not to see the belts being put in, and what they would be use for) was: What were those time and motion men doing, timing the Volvo dumpers, when everybody and his mate knew the Volvo dumpers would not be required, or for that matter, the drivers?

The top brass had turned out for the meeting to sort out the problem of the bonus once and for all, it just had to be sorted out. With respect, after they had shown to us all the time and motion reports in front of them, they said they felt we could run better times. Nothing was said for a few minutes. It was then, I had to ask the question about the new belt system, and what they had in mind for the drivers. It may seem strange, but someone had unfortunately omitted to inform them about the new belt, or at least to keep them informed, just how near the work on the belt had been to completion at that time. The meeting ended after a short adjournment. When the belt had been completed and was running to capacity a bonus scheme was worked out satisfactory to both sides based on tonnage going over the belt.

At about that time we were unfortunately to experience redundancies, I believe the number of men to go would be up to twenty-two. It would be on a voluntary basis, those who wished to go could put their names forward to be considered. I must admit it had come as a bit of a blow to all of us at Kirkby Thore at that time, by now we had ourselves a new mine manager.

I myself had by this time quit parachuting and taken up sea fishing, this being very popular with a number of the lads at the mines. I had been introduced to sea fishing by my son in law, Mel. I had also tried my hand at it whilst spending a weeks holiday on the Isle of Mull, with my old mate Fred, using a rubber dinghy, from which we had some excellent catches. I had enjoyed the fishing so much I had built a small boat for the job, it being

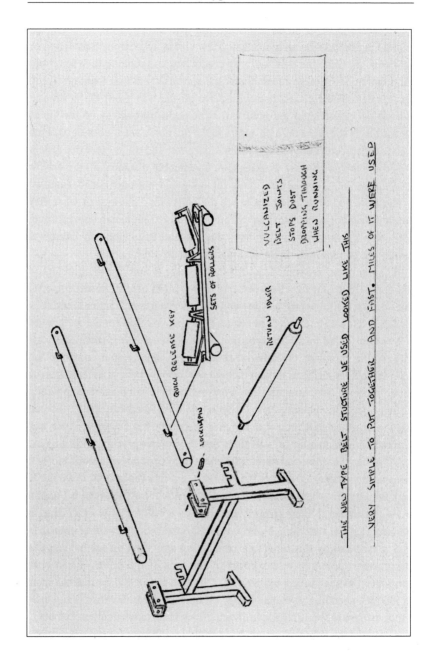

VULCANIZED BELT JOINTS STOPS DUST DROPPING THROUGH WHEN RUNNING

SETS OF ROLLERS

QUICK RELEASE KEY

RETURN IDLER

LOCKING PIN

THE NEW TYPE BELT STRUCTURE WE USED LOOKED LIKE THIS

VERY SIMPLE TO PUT TOGETHER AND FAST. MILES OF IT WERE USED

no more than ten and a half feet in length. We have spent many happy hours fishing from that boat since I first built it in 1980. That boat is only now having its first repaint job, it is now just thirteen years old, in excellent condition, and the paint work hardly damaged at all. I think my wife had been pleased by my decision to quit parachuting, and quite happy to see me take an interest in sea fishing, I had even persuaded her to come out in the boat although she hates water. I should say now, I am very lucky to have a wife as tolerant as mine has been, to put up with me for the last thirty-eight years.

When the new manager had taken over, he had been very keen to introduce to us a change in the explosive used in Longriggs Mine. This had been resisted for quite some time for health and safety reasons; we had become accustomed to using a cartridge type powder. Over the years we had tried a selection of different explosives, but for one reason or another had preferred the cartridge type, it being clean to handle. In the past, slurry types of explosive had been tried out in the mine, this it had not been popular with those of us who had used it, being dirty to handle. The type of explosive the manager wished to introduce, anfo, would reduce the cost of explosive by a significant amount. It could also be made up on site by ourselves, or rather by a man appointed to do it, in a building approved for that purpose. After many meetings with management, agreement would finally be reached, and we would use anfo explosive. This type of explosive had been in use for a number of years in other company mines, one of the mines being in the Kirkby Thore group, Newbiggin Mine, producing anhydrite. This mine had in fact used this particular type of explosive for some time. At a later date a quarry would be opened at the back of Newbiggin Mine, know as Houtsay Quarry. This quarry would provide a very high quality gypsum and it would be worked for longer than had at first been anticipated, it had been opened very close to the site of one of the original gypsum quarries, Acorn Bank. This quarry had been worked in 1880 and had also been mined later. In 1980 all the miners at Kirkby Thore had been given a rather nice glazed stoneware beer mug, made at the local Wetheriggs Pottery, with the words 'British Gypsum Mining 1880–1980'. The mugs had been given to us to celebrate on hundred years of mining at Kirkby Thore.

With the introduction of anfo, charging as we knew it would never be quite the same again. We had become accustomed to using a cartridge type explosive, and for a number of years now these had been the larger eight ounce sticks. Because the drills being used on the Secoma drill rig were nine feet in length, we had found this particular type of explosive very convenient to charge the shot holes with. Not only were they convenient for us to use they were also clean to work with, and it had been only natural for us to want to continue using this explosive. However, in light of the redundancies and the need to reduce costs, agreement was reached to begin using anfo.

Because this type of explosive is on the loose grained type, a machine would first have to be converted to enable the charger to load the shot holes. The machine chosen for that purpose had been the Chaside tractor already used for scaling and charging. The fitters had firstly to make a pressure vessel, this would be mounted on the back end of the cage on the Chaside tractor, this vessel would contain the anfo. Because of the danger of premature explosion from static electricity on the face of the drift being charged, this we had been told could be caused whilst loading the shot hole with anfo, the face and shot holes would have to be damped down with water prior to charging. Before the shot holes could be charged a water pipe with a spray fitted in the end, would first be pushed to the bottom of each hole to be charged, thoroughly damping that hole. After this had been done, another pipe would be pushed down the shot hole, anfo would then be pumped into the shot hole under pressure through this pipe. When enough anfo had been pumped into the hole the flow of anfo could be stopped by using one of two buttons controlling a valve on the bottom of the pressure vessel. The charger had to have the small control valve with the two buttons, with two small air pipes attached clipped onto his belt whilst charging that drift. A couple of claycocks tamped up behind the anfo completed the job. The claycocks, or stemming being used were purchased from a company making them for this purpose, nice soft clay inside a soft polythene cover. We had in the past used another type of stemming made of compressed sand, very prone to damage during handling, about one third would be too damaged for use by the time we came to use it.

The lads on charging would now need to check before taking the charging tractor out at the start of the shift, to be sure enough water had been put into the tank now fitted to the tractor. The anfo would be collected from the underground reserve station, with a Fordson tractor towing a trailer designed and approved for the purpose along with stemming and anything else required. The anfo came to us ready mixed in forty kilo plastic type churns, most of us found these quite heavy to lift up to the pressure vessel on the tractor, when filling the pressure vessel with anfo. The pipes used to load the anfo had to be made of a special anti-static material. The first week or two using this type of explosive reduced the amount of drifts being fired, and took us some time to get used to. As far as I was concerned it was filthy stuff to work with in a confined space, and anyone who would disagree with that statement should work with it for a month. In all the time I used anfo I certainly didn't like using it. I feel sure the reader, from the description I have just given above of the procedure involved in charging a drift using anfo, can see why we may have been so reluctant to change over to this method of charging, compared to the method we had been accustomed to.

In addition to this many changes had by this time been taking place. We were now carrying on our belts, self rescuers, introduced by the previous manager; some of us were now using airstream helmets with a battery operated mini fan in the back. The battery for this also clipped onto our belts, along with the cap lamp battery; many of the lads also carried adjustable spanners, and other tools required in the course of their work. From my own point of view the airstream helmets were very good for charging with the anfo explosive and excellent for drilling, although having said that not everyone would agree, some of the lads preferred to use the light weight masks.

Progress had been made, to cut down the dust wherever possible with the use of water bowsers. By this time, new health and safety regulations had made the lads more aware of the need to take care of their health. It all seemed a long time since I had been known in the Well Drift as that t—t, with the mask and gloves on, by now it had become the norm for everyone to wear a mask of one sort or another, gloves, ear protectors against noise, safety boots, barrier creams and hand cleansers, safety specs, even wash-hand basins at the bait cabins with hot and cold water, smart wood benches and tables, and I believe by now we had mini cookers at the bait cabins along with the telephone system. What a lot of puffs we had turned into, from the days we had sat down on a plank amongst the dust, to eat bait with mucky hands, absolutely knackered. It had taken a long time to appreciate

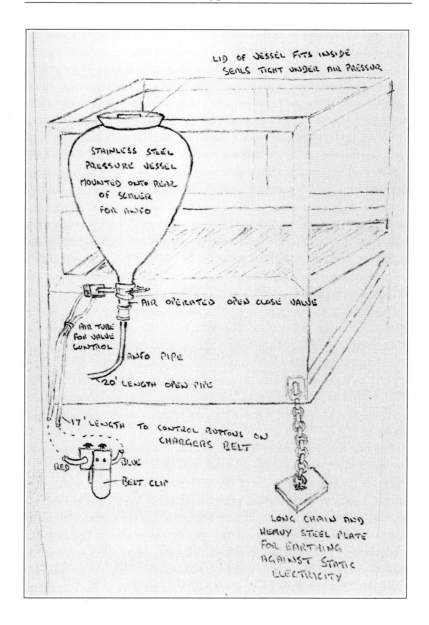

the health of the worker needed to be looked after, thankfully someone had at last had the good sense to implement some changes.

At about this time I believe we had lost some of the working faces, due to the poor quality of the rock in those loading in those faces the old vibrators had been taken out. We were now into face crushers. I should explain, the face crusher being simple to load into, the driver only had to drive up and tip onto a drag chain passing under the rotary crusher, the rock having been broken down carried on to the end of the drag chain where it dropped onto the belt that took it on its way to the crusher. It did not require a man to stand and break oversize pieces, or to switch it on and off, as with the vibrator, at times the loader may have to stop and watch large pieces through to make sure they did not jam the crusher. He would also answer the telephone, installed at that point should there be a message for him or someone else, a flashing light signalled to him the telephone was ringing.

The lower level

By this time we had built a new bait cabin in the north-east workings. We had also begun loading rock with a much larger machine, the GHH; this front end loader was very much lower to the ground than the previous machines had been, and had a much larger bucket. It was also much longer in length than any machine we had used in the mine before for loading. A powerful machine, it certainly could shift rock onto that belt. The GHH we had at this time had come to us in a very dilapidated state from one of the company mines, I don't know which one; our fitters had to do a lot of work to get that machine in a fit condition for us to use. When it had been reconditioned, and even repainted, it looked very tidy. We would work the north-east area for quite some time, and a considerable amount of rock would be mined out of this area.

I noticed at this time the morale of the men was nowhere near what it had been previously; they were concerned about redundancy and worried about how long the mine would last, the talk being that it was well past its sell by date now. The manpower at the mine had been gradually reduced with some of the older men taking early retirement, and some taking voluntary redundancy.

117

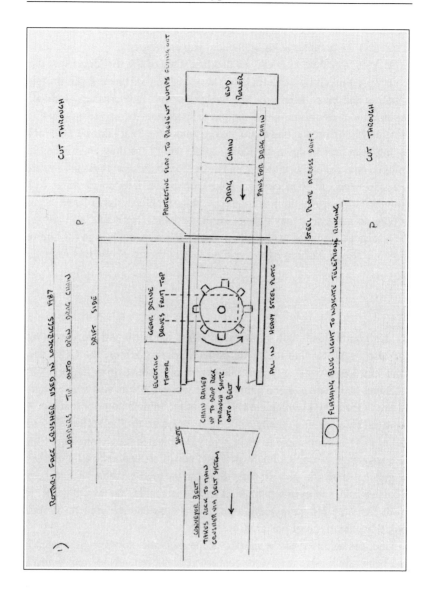

ROTARY FACE CRUSHER USED IN LONGRIGGS 1987

LOADERS TIP ONTO OPEN DRAG CHAIN

DRIFT SIDE

CUT THROUGH

P

ELECTRIC MOTOR

GEAR DRIVE DRIVES FROM TOP

CHAIN RAISED UP TO DROP ROCK THROUGH SHUTE ONTO BELT

ALL IN HEAVY STEEL PLATE

SHUTE

CONVEYOR BELT TAKES ROCK TO MAIN CRUSHER VIA BELT SYSTEM

PROTECTIVE FLAP, TO PREVENT LUMPS FLYING OUT

DRAG CHAIN

PAWS FOR DRAG CHAIN

END ROLLER

STEEL PLATE ACROSS DRIFT

CUT THROUGH

P

FLASHING BLUE LIGHT TO INDICATE TELEPHONE RINGING

118

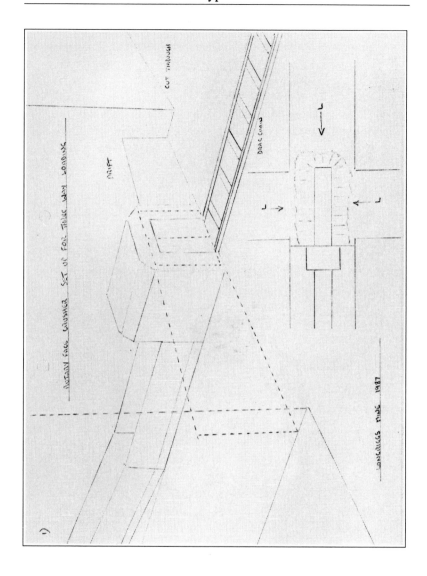

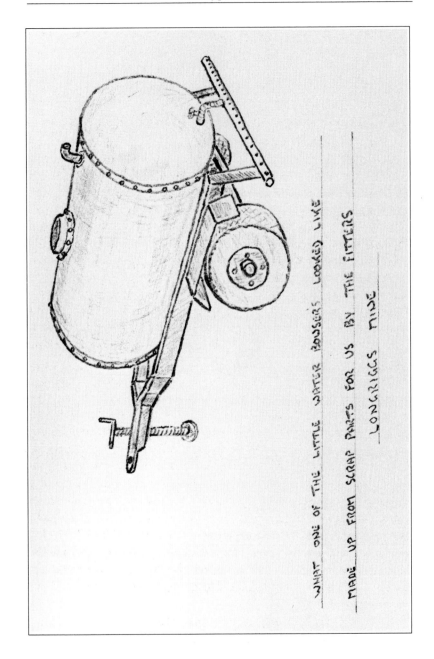

WHAT ONE OF THE LITTLE WATER BOOSTERS LOOKED LIKE

MADE UP FROM SCRAP PARTS FOR US BY THE FITTERS

LONGRIGGS MINE

It was about this time, Wilf our under-manager came to see me; he came to ask me if I would go back onto the drill rig. I must admit I was surprised at this, due to the fact that I had not been on the rig for quite some time, but said yes I would. I would be drilling in the lower level. Two drifts had been driven down at around one in five, the first had been from thirty-one cross cut, this had to be abandoned due to water; the second had been started in about thirty-four cross cut. At the time I started drilling, this drift had already been driven down below the old workings but only for a few yards, the heading being to the north, at the point where work had begun, the roof had been scaled and roof bolted as well as having steel mesh bolted to the roof and sides of the drift to prevent any scale dropping. The old workings I would now be mining below were situated at the bottom of the one in eight hill where the two drifts had been driven below the railway. The very first drifts we had driven into the north-east district a number of years previously, the reason for wanting to mine below these workings being the very high quality of the gypsum that had been found there when test boring had taken place. The rest of the lads would be working in the north-east headings, minus two men, being myself and a loader. We would work the lower level and two of the lads on the other shift would also work the lower level.

The first shift I put in on the drill rig seemed an age. I had to familiarise myself with the rig, and it was almost like starting all over again. The rig—a Secoma—seemed cumbersome although the floor was nice and flat, it had been modified by this time, having been fitted with a dust collector for each boom, at the rear of the rig the two dust collectors had been bolted on, one on each side. It seemed to me at the time, whenever I wanted to move the rig, I might hit the dust collector on the side of the drift, and it took a while for me to get used to. The dust collectors did a good job, a four inch suction pipe being fastened to each boom, when the boom was pushed against the face prior to drilling, the suction pipe would be at the point where the hole would be bored into the face. While the hole was being bored the dust pouring from the hole would be sucked into the pipe and into the dust collector. At intervals the collector would drop the dust into a pile on the floor of the drift.

It was obvious from the start that conditions here in the lower level would be rough to say the least; the further it was driven in the worse it became,

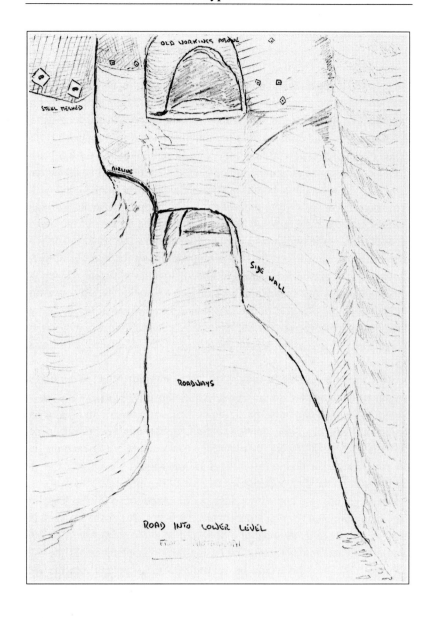

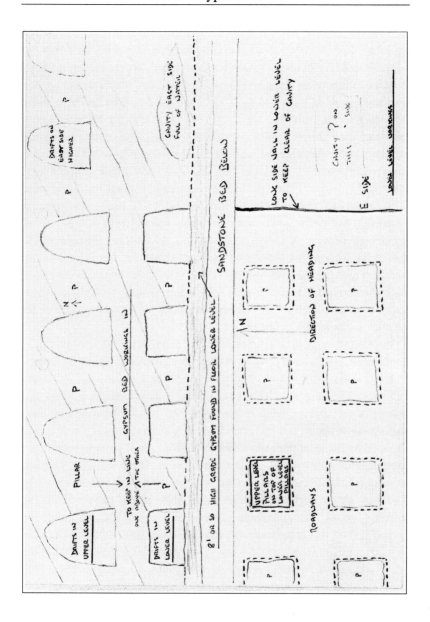

both for myself and my mate on the loader, just as it was for my old workmate Ronnie, who drilled the lower level on the other shift, and his loader. I should explain the reason for this: in the first instance it had been intended to drive two drifts into the lower level; one would be the airway, allowing the air to follow us in. Then when cut throughs had been made between the two drifts, and work had progressed enough, brattices would have been built between the two drifts allowing air to circulate through the workings and out through the second drift which would have been the return airway. Unfortunately when the first drift had been driven in some way, water had been hit in the drift, probe holes had been put in, and a water filled cavity had been hit; work in this drift had to be stopped and a pump installed. It had then been decided to take only one drift into the lower level, the one we were now working, and we could not take any drifts off to the east of the working for fear of hitting more water and tapping the cavity there already. Care would have to be taken with the pillars in the lower level, the surveyors would come at regular intervals to check the drifts for centre, and take careful measurements to ensure we kept our pillars under the ones in the workings above us.

We had a simple system of work in the lower level: at start of shift, I would bar down the drift or drifts that had been drilled and fired by Ronnie on the previous shift; when I had completed this, I would then set to and drill what drifts had been loaded out on the previous shift, a heading and perhaps a cut through; while I was doing this the loader would be busy loading out those drifts I had scaled down. Whilst the loading was taking place, the build up of fumes and dust in these confined workings would be considerable, even with the airstream helmet on. There was also the build up of heat off the tractor to contend with. At times I would be forced to walk out of the workings, and sit for a while in the fresher air in the workings above, before I could continue my work. The lad doing the loading had the advantage here, because he would get the benefit of better air every time he came out from the lower workings to tip his load at the face crusher in the upper workings. In the meantime, having completed the drilling, I would now have to charge the drifts I had bored. A barrel type fan had to be installed early on in the lower level, this would be effective for only a short time though.

Work in the lower level had by now gone very well. It had been decided to bore a series of holes through the floor from the upper workings into the lower level in the hope of improving conditions in there; the lads who did the test boring in the mine were now engaged in this work.

It was around this time I received a phone call at my home, I was on the back shift that week. I took the call at about noon, the call had been from our under-manager, Wilf. He informed me there had been a serious accident in the Newbiggin Mine, two men had been killed and the foreman injured, would I report to Longriggs office, where I would be taken from there to Newbiggin Mine along with the union convenor and himself. I was so stunned by what he had just told me I can't remember what I said, apart from that I would come right away. When I arrived at Longriggs office, I was met by George, the convener, and Wilf. We were taken in a Landrover to the Newbiggin Mine, it was the first time I had ever been to that mine. We had to wait until the police had taken statements before we entered the mine. As Longriggs Mine shop steward I was also a safety representative, as were all shop stewards, and I had been asked to do a workman's inspection at the site of the accident on behalf of the union. That day would be one of the saddest of my life, and one I shall never forget.

Work in the lower level would be pushed on now, we had been told when it had been taken as far as intended and we stopped. We would then be able to take at least six feet out of the floor due to it being of such good quality. After almost a year mining the lower level, work would come to a stop; by this time it would be about nine pillars in length and three pillars wide, or something like one hundred and thirty yards in length by fifty yards wide, approximately. We were surprised really, the work had gone very well, and we did not take out the floor as we had expected to, after all. Both Ronnie and myself and the two loaders would now be engaged on a new development, two drifts would be driven to the east from a point close to where the lower level had been driven in. The two development drifts would be taken uphill at about one in eight, one drift in thirty-one cross cut, and one drift in thirty-three cross cut. We were quite excited at this thought, the reason being we had always been told there was a lot of good rock to be had on this side, if we ever got to it.

The heading we would now be taking would take us in the direction of the old Stamphill Mine, and the black planting, where the good rock was said to be, the black planting being in fact a small wood on the surface. A

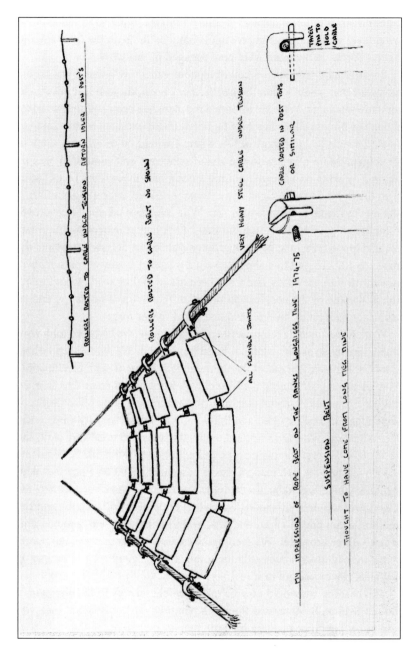

ROLLERS BOLTED TO CABLE UNDER TENSION, RETURN IDLER ON POST'S

ROLLERS BOLTED TO CABLE UNDER TENSION ON SHOULD

VERY HEAVY STEEL CABLE UNDER TENSION

ALL FLEXIBLE JOINTS

TAPER PIN TO HOLD CABLE

CABLE ROUTED IN POST TOPS OR SIMILAR

MY IMPRESSION OF ROPE BELT ON THE BANKS LONGRIGGS MINE 1974-75

SUSPENSION BELT

THOUGHT TO HAVE COME FROM LONG MINE MINE

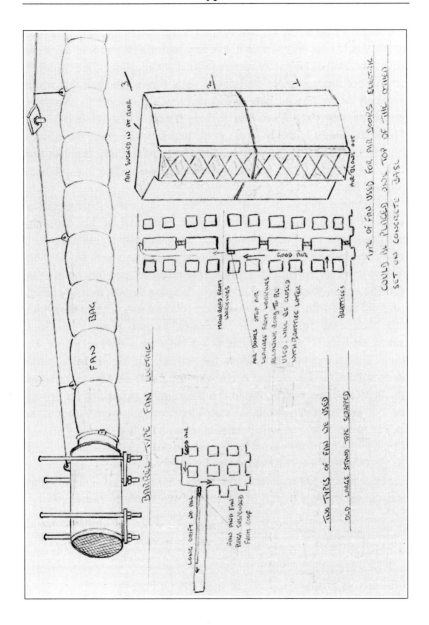

start would be made on the two drifts, I would take thirty-one cross cut, Ronnie would take thirty-three; it was only logical really to take these two drifts in particular, they were no more than a continuation of the two drifts that had been driven under the railway years before. The belt that would eventually be put into the new district and which we, hopefully, would be opening up, would run down from there in Ronnie's thirty-three cross cut, to join onto the belt already in use in the return airway under the railway, also thirty-three cross cut. What we didn't know at that time was just how hard a slog it was going to be just to drive those two drifts up the hill to the promised land.

A short time after we had started to drive the two drifts, some modification to the Secoma drill rig would take place; instead of the dust collectors the rig would be fitted with a water tank, this would supply the water for a new system called air mist, which simply put water to mix with the air under pressure down the hole running through the drill steel, coming out as a fine mist. The system itself worked quite well, damping the hole as it was bored, it also did away with the cumbersome dust collector unit that had been fitted to the back of the rig. One difference we would notice, to make the system work, a separate ½″ air hose would now have to be carried on the rig. Up to now I have said very little about the Secoma drill rig and what it was like to drill with. The rig had been built using a Track Marshall tracked vehicle, two booms were mounted at a point just to the rear of the driving seat, one on each side. Two heavy duty electric motors were built into the rear end to drive the hydraulic pumps, along with the large capacity oil tank to contain the hydraulic oil, all this added considerably to the total weight. The gearbox had been blanked off many years before, when the rigs had been quite new, it had been found that driving around the mine in the higher gears caused damage to part of the vehicle, this not only cost money but also took a lot of time to repair. The rigs could now only be driven in one low forward gear, and one low reverse gear, making their progress around the mine, should any distance be involved, rather ponderous. The booms could be operated individually by using sets of levers mounted on both sides of the driving position, and two rows of control buttons mounted in front of the driver, about twenty-four levers in all with separate levers to control air, and about twelve buttons in all. The booms were very versatile and easy to manipulate using the levers and buttons put there for that purpose. To me it was a treat to use if all was well with the machine, on the minus side the power cables were heavy to lift and drag about, at the best of times. Pulling it back when drilling had been completed after it had been pulled out in loops, it could be coiled onto the back of the machine, adding to its weight. In all it was a good rig in its time, and the two rigs we had at Longriggs owed us nothing, like most machines they wear out in the end and have to be replaced with a new one, the same fate that would happen to the men who used them.

While we were engaged on drilling the two drifts, we were informed of the death of our under-manager, Wilf. This came as a shock to us all, he would be sadly missed, having been a very popular man in all the mines and a gentleman to those who worked under his supervision. A young man took over his duties as under-manager, to us he would be known as Sher-lock—no disrespect intended, simply because he had the same name as a certain gentleman who had lived in Baker Street, London, well known for solving crimes. The young man in question was a rock mechanic or, if you like, a geologist, he had spent a lot of time earlier learning all the jobs in the mine, working with us. A short time after I left Longriggs Mine, he would go on to become manager of the most modern mine in the company.

By now we had driven the two drifts uphill at one in eight, until we almost went through the top of the seam, at which point we began descend-ing at about one in eight. The cut put through to link each drift had been put through at approximately every hundred yards, each cut through thirty-five yards long, all the way up the hill, and would be the same going down the hill. We had also brought our airline up with us, this had been hung from roof bolts heated and bent for this purpose, in the roof of thirty-one drift. Power for the drill rig being electric would also be brought in with us, the same as anywhere else in the mine, heavy duty power cables that also had to be suspended from the roof using steel wire tightened up with turnbuckles, the heavy cables were then hung in leather straps hooked onto the steel wire. We would also need to bring in a transformer shortly and as usual a small cut would be fired into the side of the drift to accommodate this. The rock we had been driving through in these two development drifts had been very hard, it was also rubbish, and had to be tipped way into the old workings at the bottom of the hill. I had been quite surprised to see just how tight the drivers had managed to pack all this rock into those old workings. It had been a hard slog for them, just as it had been for us drilling the stuff.

We had employed the same system of work we had used in the lower level: we would bar down what had been fired on the previous shift, and clear it for loading, then I would drive the drill rig into the heading set up and begin to drill that heading. My mate on this job, Kenny lad, would then begin to load the cleared drift out, taking it all the way to the bottom of the hill to dump it. In the meanwhile I would get on and get the heading scaled and loaded by the previous shift bored. By the time I had finished this—and because of the hardness of the rock it took me some time to complete— Kenny would have been to collect the powder I required to charge with. After he had given me a hand to put the powder onto the Chaside tractor, he would go back to finish loading out and I would get on with charging, we would have enough time to complete our work during that shift. The problems arrived as they always do, when we came to the point where we were to fire a cut through from one drift to the other. At this place I would not only have the heading to drill and fire after scaling the drifts fired on the previous shift, I would also have to start the cut through off as a flanker. This in itself was simple enough, all I had to do to bore the flanker was finish drilling the heading and back the drill rig up to where I had marked up for the flanker; this I would do using the spray paint we now used for this purpose. I would mark up the centre and the sides of the cut through, then I would make a mark for each hole I intended to bore. I had to do this to save time, it was not easy to see off the rig just where I was positioning the boom, and I could only use the one boom to put the holes in with. With one boom set against the side of the drift on my right hand side, I could then roll over the boom on my left hand side until it was crosswise in the drift, this allowed me to bore the holes in the flanker. After I had put the first few holes in, I would then have to reposition the rig to finish the job off. Drilling the flanker using the one boom would take time I could ill afford, but it would have to be done. Having finished drilling the flanker, I could now pull the rig out and park it up in the cut through out of line of the shots to be fired, ready for the next shift to take out. My job now would be to charge the heading and the flanker, this also would take time; if I was lucky and the lad on the loader had finished loading out he would give me a hand to charge, he was of course a shotfirer himself.

I make a point of mentioning the fact that the lad doing the loading out, Kenny, was a shotfirer. I mention this because, by this time, all the men on the highest grade of pay were flexible, and could be asked to do any job. When we had started these two drifts off we had asked why they had to be driven uphill, we had been told that test bore holes had proved the rock we were to drive through was exceptionally hard. It had later been explained to me that it was hoped that by driving the two drifts up at about one in eight, we would keep in softer rock, and get to where we wanted to be much quicker. So far the rock had been hard, but not too bad to drill with the Secoma rig, and its two rotating scroll drill steels, with a separate bit that fitted into the ends of the steels; we had no percussion on the drill motors.

We were now about sixty yards, going down at about one in eight from the top of the hill, the rock becoming harder and harder, it also began to change colour to a dark brown. The drill bits, being the rotary type, were being used by now at the rate of four on a drift, and often more, this rock just chewed them up, knocked them into a ball. We did not have to worry about bad roofing in this rock, it was solid all right, although roof bolts would be put in if necessary. The roof bolts we were now using were different from the old type we had used, those we now used were held in by resin, the old type had been held in with steel shells screwed up tight, the same as a rawl bolt. To save time it had been decided to put in a new bait cabin for us, although we had little time to spare for bait on this job, I don't think anyone envied us on this development.

It was about this time that four of the foremen in the mines were coming up for their retirement and a notice had been put up to inform all those who wished to apply for these positions to do so. Myself, and I think about fourteen others, put our names forward. After some months had passed and nothing had been heard apart from many rumours we were asked to attend an interview with the mines management. I had my interview along with all the others, and a short while later we were asked to take an aptitude test. After that nothing more was heard and we had almost forgotten about it.

In the meanwhile we in the development had pushed on to a point some two hundred yards from the top of the hill, it had been one hard slog all the way. At this point both drifts would be turned at a slight angle, and from there on we hoped it would be no more than about one hundred and fifty yards or so to break into gypsum again. We were getting excited at the

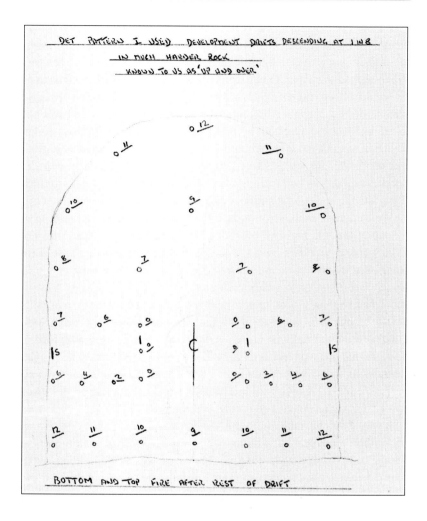

132

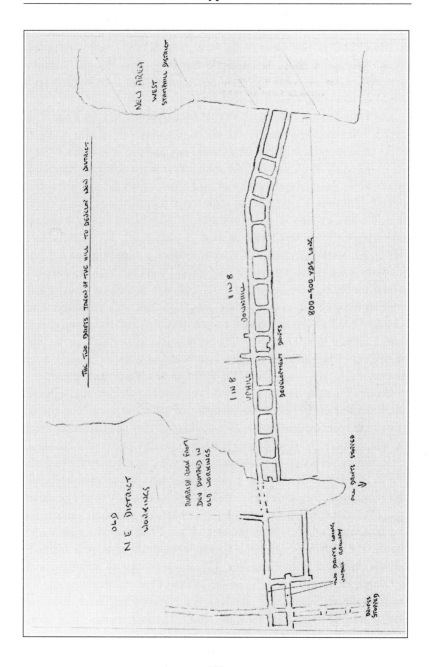

thought of this, and could hardly wait to get there: would it be a thick bed of white rock, or just some of the best gypsum ever found?—only time would tell. We were in fact not too far away from the old Stamphill workings. Later on when this new development had been opened up, it would be known as West Stamphill District.

I had finished my shift which had not been a particularly good one, I had already had one or two run ins with the mine manager about men riding out of the mine on vehicles when they should not, and one or two other things. As I walked up the hill out of the mine towards the changing rooms and office block, the manager stood waiting for me. I thought, not again, what will it be this time. He stopped me at the top of the hill. 'Can I have a word?' he said. 'Yes, as long as it doesn't take till after two o'clock,' I snapped back. 'It won't take that long,' he said, 'I want you to be the foreman at Newbiggin Mine.' I must admit, it came as quite a surprise to me and I did not know what to say. Of course I accepted. I had been asked to keep it to myself for the time being, which I did, although at times it was difficult, amid all the speculation at that time about who had been promoted. I had been told I had no chance because no one over forty had even been considered, I had just turned fifty-two. The lad who had taken me down the mine on my very first shift, Edwin, had also been made up to foreman a few months previously, when one of the four foremen, Ernie, had retired.

On looking back now over the nineteen years I had now worked in the mines, I could hardly believe the changes that had taken place. The past two years I had spent on development work, although they had been a hard slog, I think had been the best. I thought back to the day I arrived at Stamphill Mine looking for work, and had been set on there and then by Herbert who was in charge that day, and how new starters now had to have interviews and a medical. If they were lucky enough to get a start, they would be trained by a TWI man in the mine, on each job or whatever they were suitable for, and go straight onto a job on the face. When I had started a man always started on a vibrator or belt cleaning, and it could take some time before he had the chance to do anything else. The new machines we now used, even in Longriggs Mine we had the powerful Toro front end loader which had replaced the old GHH, this machine had replaced the Terex front end loaders we had been using for many years. The face crushers now in use had replaced the old vibrators. When we had changed over to charging with anfo we had used an old Chaside converted for us; this had been replaced with a machine called a Normet, used for charging and roof scaling. We had used the old Chaside and the GHH in the development drifts, the old Muir Hill tractors and trailers, the Volvo dumpers, and hand machines were now a thing of the past. I should mention though, even now hand machines still have their use in the mines on occasions, I had used one for one shift myself in the development drifts, that would be the last time I used one.

In those nineteen years I had also seen three mines managers come and go, our present manager being the fourth and the last one I would have. I had seen the mines develop to the size they are now, and of the six gypsum mines that had been working in the Eden Valley that I knew of, Cocklakes, Long Meg, Newbiggin, Longriggs, Stamphill, and Birks Head, only three remaining working at this time, these being at Kirkby Thore. I can remember the time when Longriggs Mine had produced the bulk of the rock used in the plant, and we fired as many as fourteen drifts on a shift to keep it up. As the mighty Birks Mine geared itself up to become the main production mine, we at Longriggs began to decline. As production increased from Birks Mine, so ours at Longriggs would become less. There was also the new Houtsay quarry producing a high quality gypsum, to be blended with the output from the mines, to make the top quality boards and bagged plaster that we at Kirkby Thore were noted for throughout the country. I shall also remember all those fine lads who, over the years, I had been privileged enough to have worked with, who are no longer with us.

It was the annual shut down apart from those who had permission to work, and time for holiday. I would be spending a week of my holiday sea fishing on the Isle of Mull, I had been told to report to Birks Head Mine on my return. I had resigned as shop steward, having done that job now for some nine years, when I told our convener I had accepted the position of foreman at Newbiggin Mine. For me, being shop steward had been one of the most interesting periods of my life; I had set off as a bit of a rough diamond at first, but had soon had the rough edges knocked off. I have said earlier I don't think I was ever known as a militant type, either by the lads it had been my duty to represent, or by the management, but I will admit to being ruthless at times in my negotiations with management on behalf of those men I had represented. To be a good shop steward, in my humble opinion, the man doing that job would have to be able to take it as well as

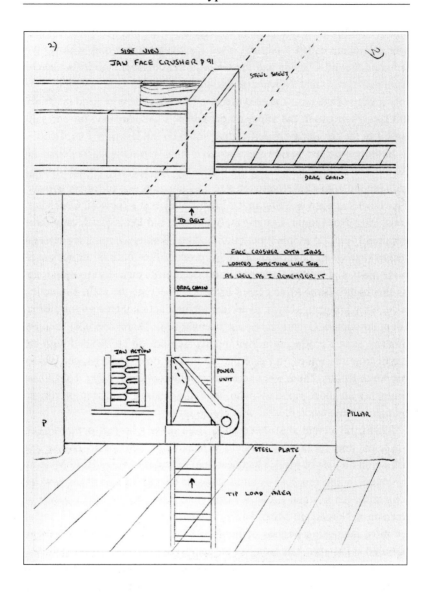

dish it out in any negotiations, be aware of the facts, do his homework beforehand thoroughly, and only fire a broadside at the opposition when he was sure it would have the most effect. It's difficult to argue against the truth.

I duly reported to the Birks Head Mine after the holiday period. Having already been given my new white helmet with my name on it, I took this with me, all mines management had white helmets. I could not help being reminded of a saying we had in the army, if they're useless give 'em a big hat to wear, and I must admit my hat on that day did feel too big, and I certainly felt very apprehensive. The reason for this was I had not been into Birks Mine for many years now, and the faces of many of the lads were strange to me, having never met them until now. Although the names were the same, sons of the lads I had worked with many years before, I would also meet many old and valued friends.

I would be spending that week with Maurice, who had been my foreman many years before when I had worked in this mine for a short while. I would familiarise myself with the foreman's duties with him, before taking up my position as the mine foreman at Newbiggin Mine. During that week I would get to know something of the paperwork I would shortly be doing myself; it would also be an opportunity for me to see the old place again, and to see what changes had been made since I had last worked in that mine. I was not prepared for what I was now about to see, the first thing I noticed being transport to take the lads to the workings. In the early days when I had worked in this mine, we had clocked on at Stamphill and walked from there all the way up the nine belt to the Birks Mine, through the connecting drift from the Stamphill Mine. This took almost half an hour. A new office block and changing rooms had by now been built, the joiner's shop and the blacksmith's shop were also over here, the new adit into the mine being almost next to the changing rooms.

Try as I might, I just could not picture in my mind where the old mine adit and aerial shed had been, until Maurice took me around to show me. The three foremen in this mine had the use of their own Ford tractor to enable them to get about the mine. After about the first two hours in the mine I could understand why: the mine had really been opened up in a big way in the years since I had worked there, I was completely lost in the first hour inside the mine. Maurice, driving the tractor, with myself on the seat

DRILL RIG IN OPERATION BIRKS HEAD MINE
VERY POWERFUL SINGLE BOOM 1990

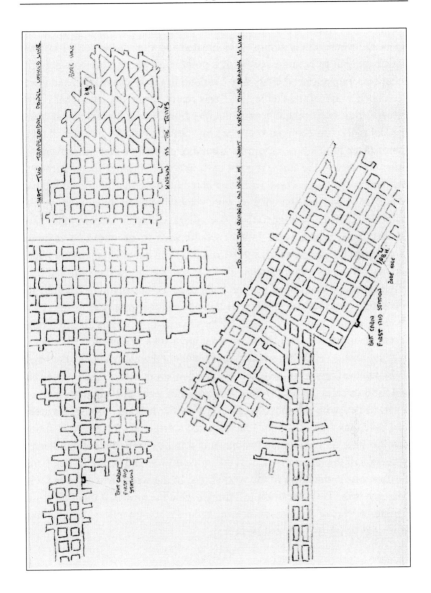

on the back, would travel from district to district. I was taken to see the wells and where all the pumps were situated and after that to see the crusher which seemed to be miles away, at a point somewhere close to where the main conveyor surfaced on its way overland to Longriggs Mine. I had never seen such a size of dust collector, I was really impressed with what I saw: the drill rigs, huge single boom jobs; the front shovel loaders. I had heard the old place had changed but I had no idea it would be like this. I think the distance at this time would be around one and a quarter miles from the mine entrance to the furthest point east, into the workings there, known to the lads as the traps. These workings here being inclined at something like one in five, and not too easy to work in, I would add. I am glad we had nothing like it at Longriggs Mine. The pillars, unlike the ones in other parts of this mine, which were square, would have to be trapezoid to make working on the incline safer; a trapezoid is a plain quadrilateral figure which has no two of its sides parallel. To us it simply means the pillars were a different shape from what we had been used to, but anything to make the job safer would be fine by us. All these workings were new to me. I had thought when I had worked here all those years ago, what a size of a mine it had been, we had about five working areas then, the north area, where I had my first go at drilling with Nipper, who incidentally still worked here at Birks, the forty-four area, and twenty-two south area, I had been on the old drott in here, the forty-four south, and the larger fifty-eight area, where I had drilled with the old Chaside rig, plus the heading, this was where I had bored my first drift after I had become a driller shotfirer. It was almost unbelievable how this mine had expanded in size from what it had been. I think one of the larger districts in this mine now would be the Knock Cross district, just to the north of the workshops. In the week I would spend with Maurice in the Birks Head Mine, I think I spent the most of it totally lost—in a mine the size of this one, something around a square mile of underground workings or more, I am not surprised.

Newbiggin Mine

I had enjoyed my week at the Birks Head, but I think I was pleased in a way, I would not be staying on there. But how would I take to Newbiggin

Mine when I finally arrived there? That I would find out on the following Monday morning at 0600 hours. Newbiggin Mine, almost next door to the village of Newbiggin, would be about two miles along a quiet back road from Kirkby Thore. The splendid view from the office window really was something to talk about, I could look out across the Eden Valley all the way to the Lakeland Fells some eighteen miles or more away. The green of the fields all around this mine only added to the charm of the whole place. As I have already stated earlier in this book, I had been into this mine on only one occasion two and a half years previously, and this had been a very sad one for me.

Looking down the road from the office, in the foreground I could see the crusher and hopper housing, with a covered conveyor belt from there up to the top of the two bins that held the crushed rock and the dust. To one side of the bins there was a small stockpile of cement quality rock, this had been tipped there from the Houtsay Quarry being worked at the other side of the mine which had been working now for around two years. The quarry produced a very high quality gypsum, but in order to extract the gypsum they first had to remove the anhydrite off the top of the gypsum bed. This had to be tipped onto stockpile out of the way until required for use. At the time I came to the mine, some of this stock rock had already been used, from the stockpile I could see from the office. To me it would be completely different from what I had been used to in the other mines I had worked at. In the first instance there were no conveyor belts in use at this mine other than the one on the surface, from crusher to bins. All the rock produced from this mine would be brought to the surface using tractor trailer units, these would tip their loads into the hopper on the surface, and a drag chain would then feed the rock into the rotary crusher. After the rock had been crushed it would then drop onto the conveyor belt that would take it to the top of the bins, there it would drop onto a vibrating screen, this screen would shake most of the dust or fines onto a short cross belt. The screened rock would drop off the screen into the bin or hopper below, the dust or fines would feed into a smaller separate bin on the side of the main bin off the cross belt. A haulage contractor would drop the crushed rock out of the bottom of the bin and transport it to the works at Kirkby Thore, where it would be processed.

The rock from Newbiggin Mine would be graded into two types, one would be cement grade rock, and one would be used in the manufacture of a product known to us as Anpak, the rock for this product would have to be of high quality anhydrite. This would also be sent to a glass manufacturer, the cement grade rock would be taken away from the works in wagons to the cement company. It would be my responsibility to ensure I was sending the correct grade of rock to the surface each day. The foreman in charge of the mine had been asked to stay on for a further six weeks, until he officially retired; this would enable me to get the feel of the mine, become familiar with the rock types, and allow me to settle in more easily. This type of mining was completely different from what I had been accustomed to at Longriggs Mine, and would naturally take me a little time to get used to. The roofs were very much lower and always fired flat. I would have to learn the difference between cement grade rock and Anpak quality rock fired in the drifts. Joe, the foreman, would teach me this before he retired. Newbiggin Mine worked one shift only, six to two, unlike the other mines, so if we had any problems it could not be left for the next shift in to sort it out, we would have to sort any problems out ourselves, and this suited us fine. As I have already said the mine produced two types of rock, to put it simply, anhydrite would go for Anpak production; the same rock but with a higher percentage of gypsum in it would be graded as cement rock, having too much gypsum in it to be sent as Anpak quality. I will do my best to explain the difference: anhydrite $Ca.SO_4$: Calcium sulphate. Gypsum $CaSO_42H_2O$: Hydrous calcium sulphate. Both being sedimentary rocks, the anhydrite beds at Newbiggin would average about ten feet in thickness, it was harder to drill than the gypsum at Longriggs Mine. I found anhydrite to be coarse grained, very dark grey in colour, after it had been fired, it looked almost black and sparkled in the light of a cap lamp, but had a lovely mixture of colour I find difficult to describe, from a lovely pinkish colour through to a light brown and streaks of almost colourless rock. It was a very heavy rock with a gravity of 3.0, and a hardness of 3–3.5. Some of those who supplied us with drill steels considered the rock to be very soft for drilling, but in practice the coarse grain of the rock combined with the water whilst drilling a shot hole, seemed to me to have a grinding paste effect and soon ground the drill bits down. The rock itself when held in the hand felt like a piece of porcelain, struck with a hammer it shattered into very sharp pieces. I liked to pick a piece up in the drift and hold my lamp behind it just to see the beautiful display of colours as the light shone through the rock. Compared to the gypsum I worked in at Longriggs Mine, this really was a lovely rock. It was easy to see the gypsum bed. After a drift had been fired, it could be seen at the base of the drift. If the driller had sunk his drills in too deep, which he tried to avoid doing, there might be as much as eight inches or so of the gypsum bed below the anhydrite beds exposed. Providing it was no more than this, that rock could go for Anpak, if it were much more than this, it would have to be sent out as cement rock.

It would take me a while to become familiar with this, but after a time I could soon tell what drifts could or could not go out as Anpak or cement. The bed of anhydrite we were mining out would be about ten feet thick, and the thicker it was the better for us. At times it would drop down to seven feet or sometimes even less. We would then have to fire the floor out at that point in order to proceed, it might only be a matter of a few feet, and the roof could be taken up again. On many occasions I thought we may have to stop a drift, because the roof had become low, only to find the cut through coming in at the back of the drift maintained full height, and the drift we were driving would rise to that height as it was driven forward. If we found it did not rise to that height, and vehicles could not pass unhindered through, then it would have to be permanently fenced off with No Road signs and wired off. Longriggs Mine did not have this problem; the drifts there could be as high as twenty-eight feet or more, arched in the roof, the thickness of the gypsum beds allowed this, being up to sixty or more feet thick. The gypsum beds there would be of the fibrous variety, made up of layers of the lovely white satin spar and grey marls. Gypsum being softer when it came to drilling, the shot holes could be bored with a drilling rig without the need for percussion, using the scroll type drill steels. At Newbiggin Mine they would be of little use to us, we had to have percussion to bore the shot holes in anhydrite, the only gypsum we had in our drifts being the three feet of gypsum in the floor below the anhydrite. In Newbiggin Mine, this had been taken out as flooring from the north-west side of the mine at one time, it had also been mined out as gypsum from the old north side of the mine, before flooding. The walk from the office to the mine entrance would be around four hundred yards, and at six twenty in the morning so peaceful.

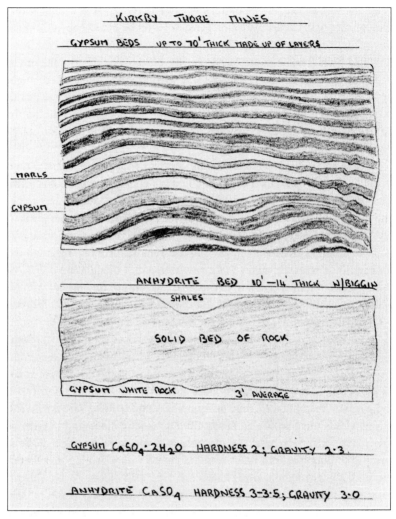

KIRKBY THORE MINES

GYPSUM BEDS UP TO 70' THICK MADE UP OF LAYERS

MARLS

GYPSUM

ANHYDRITE BED 10'—14' THICK N/BIGGIN

SHALES

SOLID BED OF ROCK

GYPSUM WHITE ROCK 3' AVERAGE

GYPSUM $CaSO_4 \cdot 2H_2O$ HARDNESS 2; GRAVITY 2.3

ANHYDRITE $CaSO_4$ HARDNESS 3-3.5; GRAVITY 3.0

It was 17 August 1987, this would be my first shift at Newbiggin Mine, we stopped to have a word with the lad who worked on the surface, on our way down the mine. It was Arty, I had worked with him many years before in Longriggs Mine. Arty had been injured there when the cage on the old Hudson scaler had broken away. It was his job to put the powder up in the kits or churns, for the lads in the mine. He would load the powder trailer up for them, and issue the dets, keep the office and changing rooms clean and tidy, and keep an eye on the rock going through the crusher, the drivers would have this to do themselves if he was on other work. He would be told what rock we were sending out on that particular shift, cement grade or Anpak, he would inform the haulage contractor of this so the drivers would know which heap to tip into over at the works.

The entrance to the mine looked small compared to the entrance to Longriggs Mine, it was set in the bottom of the old quarry, that had been worked some time before. We walked down the haulage road to the entrance and stopped to allow the first of the tractor trailer units to come out on its way to the crusher with the first load of the shift. The engine roared as it went past us loaded with rock, I could tell he had a fair weight on the trailer. The lad on the tractor gave us a wave as he passed. Joe just puffed on his pipe, and I followed as he took off into the mine. We walked straight forward for about twenty yards and then turned sharp right. I looked down the haulage road, the lights on the side of the drift twinkled for as far as I could see, steel air pipes and electric power cables fastened up to the roof. I liked the look of this mine, with its low flat roof. This is my kind of mine, I thought to myself. I almost had to run to catch up with Joe as he turned to walk down a drift to his left, with steel pipes fastened to the roof. These pipes came out of the mine workings bringing water, pumped from a small well at the back of the fitting shop. I would find out all about water in the coming months. By this time Joe had stopped at the bottom of the slope we had just walked down, there were two pumps in here, one 10 h.p. mono pump, and the 25 h.p. Worthington Simpson. This tripped on and off with a float switch, this being the wells for the South Anhydrite District of the mine. From here water would be pumped via a rising main to the small beck on the surface by the crusher.

The pump was running but had lost its suction. Joe switched it off, opened a bleed valve allowing air to escape and water to spray out, after a while he tightened the valve and switched the pump back on. Along the pipeline from the pump he opened a small tap to check water was passing through, water spurted out. 'That's okay, sometimes gets airlocked,' he said. 'Have to keep an eye on it.' He lit his pipe again, and we walked from the wells to the fitting shop, a distance of some four hundred and fifty yards. At least we had a decent fitting shop, I thought, as I had a look around, the place certainly was kept exceptionally clean. We walked over to the fitter, Cyril, who was cutting some steel plate with the burners, and I was introduced to him, I had worked with his father very briefly in the old Birks Mine, where he had been a loader on a tractor, and later worked in the underground laboratory at Stamphill. From the fitting shop Joe took me to see the two compressors just across from the fitting shop, in one of the back drifts. They were both revving away nicely, one 90 h.p. and one 160 h.p. The air pressure would be kept at a steady 100 p.s.i., the same as in the other mines. The drill rigs used in this mine were Holrigs, mounted on tracks and required plenty of air and water to keep them happy. I had not really seen one of these rigs before, but I recognised the sound of it as soon as we approached within hearing distance. At that point about three hundred yards away, just hearing that noise took me back a lot of years, hand machines, I found myself thinking, definitely hand machines. As we walked into the drift where the rig was standing, I began to understand why I had been thinking hand machines. The noise blattering away in there would be over 120 dB, with the two percussion rock drills going at the same time. The lad on the machine stopped drilling when we stood by his rig; it was Harold, one of the miners who had come to Kirkby Thore when the Long Meg mine had closed down. My ears were still ringing with the noise. He took his ear plugs out to have a crack with us. Looking at the rig from the rear end, I can only describe it as looking somewhat like a crab with both of its nippers raised. 'Asta sin owt like this afore?' Harold asked me. 'Should be in a museum,' he said before I could answer, and pushed the air control levers forward, and began to drill again.

My ears were still ringing as we walked around the corner to see the charger, Bill, whom I had met on a previous occasion when we both attended a mine rescue course at a mine rescue station near Windscale years before. I looked at the old plastic anfo loader he was using in the drift, it had been a long time since I had seen one like that, and the ladder he used to charge the top holes with. I began to think I had stepped back in time. I think the anfo loader was called a Pemburthy, or something similar. It could only hold around forty pounds of powder at a time, but was light in weight and easy to move around, and cost absolutely nothing to run, not quite like a Normet. To load the anfo, all the charger had to do was push the loading pipe into the shot hole, and squeeze the hand held air control lever. This

operated an open close valve on the Pemburthy, allowing powder to fill the shot hole, the charge would then be primed and stemmed up with a clay cock. There was no requirement to damp the holes separately using air mist because the drill rig used water to drill the holes in the first place, leaving the shot holes, the face of the drift, and even the drift itself, very wet.

We checked with Bill how many shots and drifts he would be firing at the end of shift, noted these down and went on to see the lad doing the loading. The machine used for loading the tractors looked familiar to me when I saw it, and so it should, it was a much smaller model GHH front end loader, the same type of machine we had used in the development drifts in Longriggs Mine. The driver, Harold, finished loading rock into the trailer of the Ford County tractor parked in the drift. I noticed how tight it had been for him to tip into the trailer, the bucket of the loader touched the roof during loading. Harold stopped his machine and I was introduced to him, he would be my deputy, and stand in at times when I would not be there. We had a crack for a few minutes while Harold had his smoke before another tractor arrived to be loaded up.

I should have mentioned earlier in this book, there were no regulations or prohibition of smoking in the gypsum mines at Kirkby thore, there being no dangerous gases in the mines to cause danger. Smoking was, however, prohibited wherever charging was taking place or by that person charging, and also at certain other places in the mine, and these places would have large signs up clearly stating Smoking Prohibited.

During my first shift I would be taken around all the pumps in the mine, I would need to know what type they were and just where they were situated. The 50 h.p. submersible pump in the north side of the mine would be the largest of all the pumps, Joe would take me over to see where this pump was situated. We would have to walk over to the North Anhydrite District to see the pump, the distance from the fitting shop would be between five to six hundred yards, a good walk. From where we were now standing with Harold in the north-west area of the South Anhydrite District, it would be all of three to four hundred yards back to the fitting shop. From the fitting shop we walked uphill towards the mine entrance, on our way we would have to stand to one side to allow the tractor trailer units, loaded or empty, to pass us. I noticed the lads had their own system for passing each other on their way to and from the surface to the workings. They would

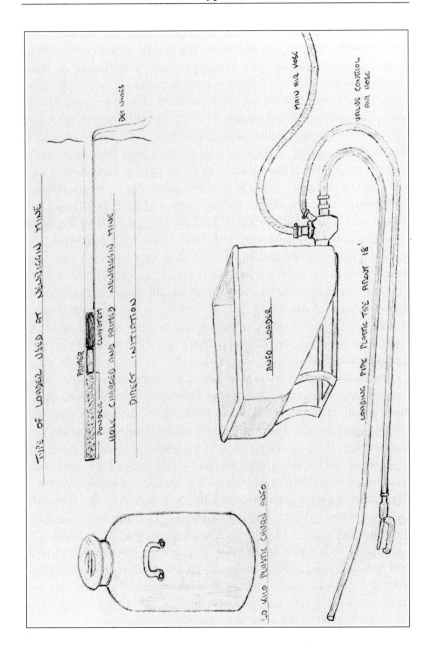

wait at certain points along the route, and also had markers at passing points, the road being only sixteen feet wide. The system worked very well for them, the tractors were not easy to manoeuvre in the confines of the mine.

When we had almost reached the mine entrance, we turned off to our right, at the same place we had been earlier to look at the pumps in the wells. This time we carried on past the mine entrance in a drift that would take us over to the north side. I noticed that in this mine there were a lot of No Road signs about; a No Road sign means danger for one reason or another, and it was standard practice in all the gypsum mines to put these signs up to stop anyone going beyond that point. The signs would be put up wherever there was danger of some kind, bad roof, water holes, and special ones used to indicate a drift had been charged ready to fire. Holes would be drilled into each side of the drift and a heavy steel wire cable would be bent over and knocked into one hole with a wooden plug, then pulled tight; another wooden plug would then be knocked into the hole on the other side of the drift, with the wire around the bottom and knocked up tight. The piece of old belting that had been cut to size, with the message NO ROAD painted in reflective paint, could be hung from the cable. All signs in the mine were prepared in reflective paint and could be seen from a considerable distance.

I stopped to look at the roof in one of the drifts as we walked along the road, and made sure I was on the right side of the No Road sign. I could see at once why the sign had been put up, the roof on the other side was hanging with a four inch gap above it. These workings had long since been worked out, all the present workings being on the other side of the mine, on the south side; we had to walk through this part of the mine to get to the three pumps that were installed permanently to stop this part of the mine from becoming flooded. Almost all the side drifts had been closed off with wire, and signs put up. There had been many roof falls in the past, I could see the heaps of rock in the drifts. The safest place on this side of the mine was the main road, which we were now walking along. The road had to be scaled as and when required because it was still in use, but only to check water levels and pumps, and that would be done by me or the electrician, and the fitters would come on occasions if repairs were required to any of the pumps. There was nothing on this side now apart from the three pumps in use, two submersibles and one 10 h.p. mono pump, the whole place being very damp and musty, smelling a bit like being in a really grotty cave.

The distance from the mine entrance to the pump would be around four hundred or more yards; at a point about midway between the pump and the mine entrance we had to walk up a slight rise in the road, the road here being very damp, we had been following almost the same route as the five inch metal bower pipes. These pipes carried the water from the 50 h.p. pump to the rising main near the mine entrance, the same rising main also took the water pumped from the well. In the light of my cap lamp, I could see tiny pin points of light reflected back to me from the floor of the drift, glittering and sparkling like diamonds in the beam of light from my cap lamp, it really was lovely to see. After I had stopped to take a better look, I could now see what it was, tiny growths of needle-like gypsum; I had seen this on only one previous occasion, in one of the Easgill Caverns, better known as the Gypsum Cavern. The needles were very brittle and fragile and easily damaged. If vehicles had been using this road regularly they would not have been there.

We carried on until we came to the 10 h.p. mono pump. Joe switched the pump on, the water from this travelled only a matter of yards before it too rose to the surface via a three inch rising main, to be discharged into the small beck on the surface. 'I will switch it off on the way back,' said Joe.

We turned a corner just then and walked through what had once been a set of doors, only the frame was left now. The doors had been put in for ventilation purposes when this part of the mine had been working. I could see a large crack in the breeze blocks of a brattice by the old frame and walked over to have a look. 'Must be a bit of weight on this,' I said to Joe. The brattice had a bulge in it like a pregnant duck. 'Could be,' he said, 'more likely to be the floor coming up though.' We hurried on to the end of the drift we had been standing in. Again I saw the bower pipes, we had left them some way back, at the corner we had turned to our left they had carried on through the old workings. I looked down a single drift that had been driven down at about one in eight. This drift had been driven down at this angle in order to get at some good gypsum that was known to be there. It had only been a few years since it had been stopped because of flooding. The 50 h.p. pump we had come to check out had been put in at that time to remove the water flooding back from these workings. If the water were not pumped to the surface it would eventually have flooded all the way back to the mine entrance, from there it would have poured down the hill into the present workings, and if left would have filled those workings right back to emerge from the mine entrance. I could see water at the bottom of the drift and the line of metal bower pipes coming back up the hill from the 50 h.p. pump. I turned to see where the pipes disappeared to from where I stood, I was in fact standing on a ridge, the one in eight drift to the pump on one side and about a one in eight dropping down into abandoned flooded workings on the other side. I could see the water was up to the roof in the old workings.

We walked down the hill to see where the pump was placed in the drift, an old raft made of oil drums that had been used to float a pump on when the workings had first flooded stood to one side. I could see the two floats that switched the pump on and off quite clearly from where I stood, I could also see the top of the pump sticking out of the water, with the metal pipes coming away from the outlet side of the pump. The water would be no more than three feet deep where I was standing; I could not tell how deep it would be further in towards the pump. Joe said the pump was about due to start up by the look of the float, there was certainly plenty of water about. We walked back up the hill from the pump and stood and looked at the gathering of water on the other side in the old workings, the light reflected from my cap lamp on the water made a pattern on the roof. It would be a long walk back to the office from here for our bait, but it had given me a better idea of what I would be taking over very shortly.

On the walk back, Joe wanted to show me where the roof had been shored up with timbers. I would need to know where to go, if I should have to check it out in the future. The whole place had a very musty smell about it, damp and cold, the roof being about twelve feet in height and very near the surface at this point. The timbers had been put in to shore up the roof in this place because it was thought the roof could cave in and let the small beck on the surface through if it did. The timbers were tight, we had a good look at them and they were no worse than the day they had been put in, although the roof in the place left a lot to be desired.

I think I was pleased to get out of that spot and breathe fresher air, this part of the mine being marked on the drawing as the stowed area. Back towards the mine entrance Joe pointed to some workings to his left. 'That's where the C Bed pump is, we will just have a look, to see if it has made any water over the weekend.' We had to walk down a slope of around one in seven to get to the pump. As we approached I could hear the pump humming away, even though it was submerged in water, about eight feet of it. The workings here had been stopped by a fault, the water had come up to the roof, but from where we were standing on the steep muddy banking I could see the remains of an old scraper sticking out of the water and the rest of it below the surface. Joe told me the outlet from this pump could be seen hanging over the dam wall in the well, and to check it was pumping every morning all I had to do was see that water was pouring from the pipe end. This place was also wet and grotty and had seen its share of roof falls, judging by the piles of roof on the floor—most of the place had No Road signs up.

The bright sunshine hit my eyes as we walked out of the mine. What a place this is for water, I thought as we walked back up the road to the office. It seemed to me water came in through the roof, through the floor, through the sides, just couldn't get away from it anywhere. I could see I was in for a good soaking in the months ahead, and I was right. During our bait time, I had time to have a good look at the mine plan on the wall, and to get a better idea of just where Joe had taken me. The main workings were now in the north-west area of the South Anhydrite District, I could see by the mine plan it would not last for very much longer, the last drifts we could take out would be in thirty-six cross cut. I could see we were running out of time fast. There were only nine headings being worked and we were already working in thirty-two cross cut, although the drifts were good and the rock was good, we stopped at thirty-six cross cut. We could not go under the railway line, and this lay in our path at this point. I could see I would need to open another area somewhere, and at this time I had no idea where.

We finished our bait and had a walk down to the crusher, it was a rotary crusher, rock feeding into it off the drag chain. I watched as Arty, the lad on the job, stopped the chain to stop the larger pieces of rock falling into the crusher. He would break them up with a large hammer. I was amazed at the size of some of the lumps that dropped into the hammers in the crusher and were smashed to pieces. Both Joe and Arty told me that when this crusher had been installed they had expected it to drop to bits within a week,

153

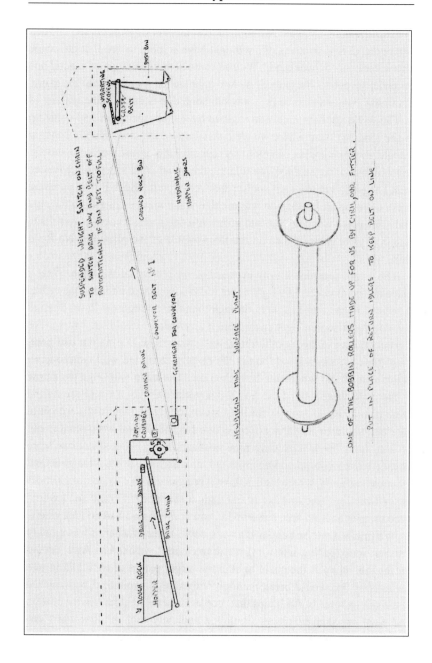

SUSPENDED WEIGHT SWITCH ON CHAIN
TO SWITCH DRAG LINE AND BELT OFF
AUTOMATICALLY IF BINS KEPT TOO FULL

UNLOADING
STATION

CROSS
BELT

DUST BIN

CONVEYOR HEAD BIN

HYDRAULIC
HOPPER DOORS

COUNTER BALANCE

COUNTER BELT No 1

GEARHEAD FOR CONVEYOR

ROTARY
CRUSHER

DRAG LINE DRIVE

DRAG CHAIN

V TROUGH DECK
HOPPER

NEWBRIDGE MINE SURFACE PLANT

ONE OF THE BOGGIN ROLLERS MADE UP FOR US BY CURNLOWE FITTER.

PUT IN PLACE OF RETURN ROLLERS TO KEEP BELT ON LINE

but here it was, still going strong. Just then another tractor load arrived, the driver backed up to the hopper and tipped his load in. I could see there were a number of very large pieces of rock that would need to be broken down before they could be dropped into the crusher, in fact one of the pieces jammed in the bottom and blocked it. Arty took an old drill steel obviously there for the job and slipped it in behind the piece of rock, pushing it down hard. As one of the flights on the chain came around, it caught against the drill steel and pulled the rock loose. When this piece had been pulled far enough up the chain on its way to the crusher, the drag chain was stopped and Arty had to give the piece of rock a good belting with the big hammer to smash it up. The next load up I had a go at smashing some of the larger pieces myself, and found while some were good to break up others were not and had to be given a right good belting with the big hammer to break them down. The dust about the place was very bad, and I could see something would have to be done to cut this down in the future. There was also a lot of dust dropping through the plates, and piling up under the drag chain, time being wasted on clearing this out during the shift.

From the crusher I was taken to the surface fan house, this was a small brick building set on top of a tubular steel air shaft, the 40 h.p. fan sat on top of the shaft. We also had a 50 h.p. fan underground, located at the bottom of a separate upcast shaft sucking air through from the return airway drift, brattices put in to form a dead end, the upcast shaft being a hole fired through the roof of a drift to the surface, in old workings, with a wall built around it on the surface covered with steel meshing. At this time both fans were in use, and the air in the mine would be the best of all the three mines now working at Kirkby Thore although, unlike the other mines, which were dry and very dusty, Newbiggin Mine was damp and cold.

I went home after that first shift with plenty to think about. This mine would have to have some changes made to it, I thought to myself, but where to start would be something else. Over the next few weeks I would have to learn as much as I could about the mine, and the running of it, being so much different from what I had been used to.

By the end of the first week I had settled down a little. I had now met all the lads working there, and Joe had taken me through most of the paperwork I would be required to do. I would not be required to work that

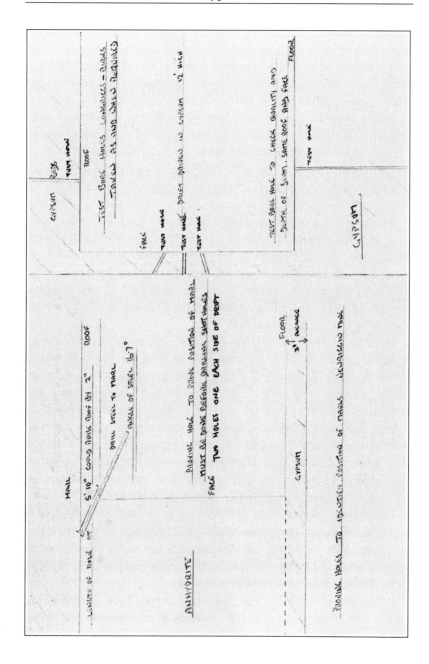

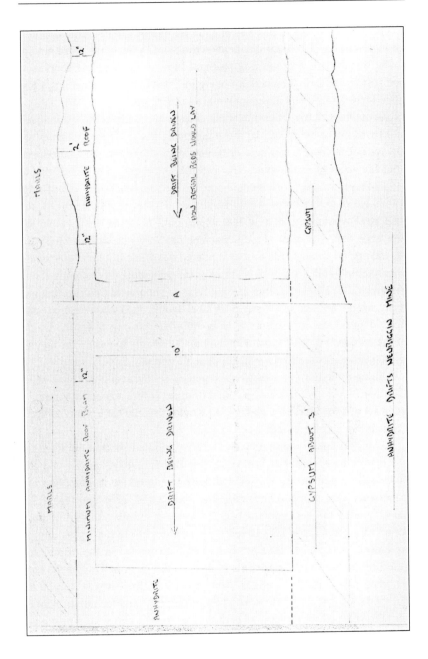

weekend and I could spend a little time on one of my favourite hobbies, making walking sticks and shepherds' crooks using tup horns. I had always found this to be a very relaxing pastime. Most of the lads had hobbies of one sort or another, stick making being just one of mine, something I had done for years and had never grown tired of doing.

I would spend the following week doing the rounds in the mine again, and I was interested to see the test holes being put in. These test holes are always put in prior to boring a drift, new regulations had been introduced after the accident in the mine. The test holes were put in to ensure that at least twelve inches of rock would be left in the roof at all times after firing. The angle of the test hole would be sixteen degrees to the horizontal, the drill steel would be run in at that angle, until it hit the marl above the anhydrite bed. The driller on the machine had to watch very carefully for the change in colour of the dust as it poured out of the test hole; this would change from white to brown, black or grey, depending on the marls above the anhydrite. He would stop the machine as soon as the colour changed from white, the length of the drill steel would then be measured and, depending on that measurement, he could either raise or lower the height of the roof in that drift. It would be my responsibility to ensure the regulations on roofs were strictly adhered to at all times.

During those first six weeks I spent getting settled in at Newbiggin Mine with Joe I knew that this was my kind of mine. It was a good little mine, a good set of lads, I liked the place, but I would certainly have plenty to think about in the coming months.

Six weeks passed and it was the last day for Joe. We had the monthly stock take to do—it was Friday 25 September 1987—and we did the stock take together. As we walked back to the office to complete the paperwork, Joe stopped and looked at me. 'I will give you these,' he said, handing me his bunch of keys. 'I won't be needing them any more now.' We had a last walk around the mine, he telling me which pumps to keep an eye on. At the end of that shift as we sat in the office, Joe filled in the books and signed them up for the last time. One of the lads knocked on the door. 'The lads want to see you, Joe.' It was Harold, he had been Joe's deputy for many years. I took my camera, and we walked into the lads' changing room. There they presented him with a new pipe, and a pack of his favourite tobacco. Joe was a tough old lad but I could see he was moved by the kindness. I took some photographs of Joe and the lads together and it was time to go home. I would attend his retirement dinner later that same evening.

During the next few weeks I would find out a lot about the mine the hard way; I would also give a lot of thought to what changes or improvements could be made to its running. One of the main things that had to be done, and as soon as possible, was to talk to Duggie, my electrician, about the pumps. He had approached me earlier about putting float switches wherever practicable. Having decided which pumps would have the float switches fitted, the switches were ordered for the job. The flooding in the north side had now been brought under control, it had taken quite a while to get the water level down to where I wanted it. I had left a small submersible pump in, which I would switch on as and when required, to keep the water level down. It had been a weight off my mind when the water had been brought under control on this side of the mine. I could now concentrate on getting the level in C Bed down. We had a lot of heavy rain which had not helped, with water pouring in at the mine entrance from the surface. Although we had a steel grid at the mine entrance to run water into a pipe to take the water to the well, we still had a lot of water running in. This caused the main haulage road to be wet and not helpful for the drivers hauling the rock out of the mine. I could see that this would be one of the improvements that would have to be made—the haulage road would have to have a lot of work done on it. The water from the small well at the back of the fitting shop arrived at the main well via a pipeline that came up the side of the main haulage road, the metal pipes were very old, most of the couplings leaked water. It had to happen—due to storms overnight the power had gone off, all the pumps had stopped and the main haulage road had flooded, and it took some time to get the water out. When this happened, as it seemed to do quite often, the switch in the sub station on the surface trips out and has to be put back in. Once that has been put in the electrician has to come down the mine to the number two sub station and put that switch back in, from there he has to go all the way around the mind putting the various switches back in to restore power for the pumps and compressors, drill rigs and water pumps for the drill rigs. All this takes up valuable time and stops production. I was beginning to see what I had taken over would give me plenty to think about, as lads were off sick and taking holidays, it would be a struggle to keep up with production, tractors breaking down, drill rigs breaking down, and a demand for more production.

We were working almost every Sunday now, some on production, some maintenance. We had made a start on the main haulage road from the surface to the workings; whenever we had a maintenance shift I would have at least one of the lads on the road, filling in holes and levelling off. We used ton after ton of Anpak dust to level the main road off, but it was getting better every time we worked on it, very soon it would be like a motorway, and this had been my intention from the start. It would be some time before it would be completed, but it would be completed come what may.

Christmas had come at last. I felt ready for a break now. I had been just three months as the mine foreman at Newbiggin Mine, and I had plenty to think back on. I realised one thing, I missed the hard work I had been used to over the past years, and on the development in the Longriggs Mine. I never thought I would, but I did. When I think back, all those years slogging with a pick and a bar every day, how I had to put my old red handkerchief with white spots on around my head, under my helmet, to stop the sweat running down my face. The hacking away at the loose rock to scale it off, the fumes off the tractors, and the smell of the anfo as I had pumped it into the shot holes, standing in a fog of dust, unable to see to put holes in the face when the air mist packed in, and having to carry on just to get finished. If anyone thinks for one moment I missed all that he must be really stupid. The job I was doing now would be a challenge to me, and one thing I liked most of all was a challenge. Here I could use my own initiative with little interference and get on with the job of making this a real good little mine. I realised very quickly I would have to get my priorities right from the start. We had now reached the point of no return in the north-west workings, having reached thirty-four cross cut. I knew we could not mine beyond thirty-six cross cut, and we would reach this point within a few months. Everything else, the water, and the water pipes, were of no importance; we had to have good rock from somewhere, if the mine were to continue producing. Since I had taken over as the mine foreman I had spent some time looking for a suitable place to open up as a new area. I had been into the old workings many times looking at the drifts, and checking the condition of the roofs and the direction of faults. Joe had shown me one drift where he thought I might eventually find good anhydrite. All the drifts in these old workings had run into faults or very poor rock and had been stopped, there were piles of roofing that had dropped out everywhere.

I had put one of the lads, Keith, drilling in the old south-east area, this had been worked after the water had been pumped out of it but had not been worked regularly. It was a very cold, damp area, and had been flooded for some time, the water mark on the side of the drifts showed how high the water level had been. This area had been pumped out, and a water catchment put in to contain the water that came up through a hole in the floor, a pump had been installed there and pumped the water to another water catchment at the back of the fitting shop, from where it was pumped to the main well. Some work had been done but very little. What Keith fired in this area had to go as cement rock, due to the amount of gypsum in the rock being close to the outcrop of the beds. I would keep Keith drilling and firing this area as much as I could, I had decided this would be the new main working area when the north-west came to a stop. I only hoped I would find some good quality anhydrite in there. I would have to have enough room for all the lads to work when the north-west came to a stop. All I could do for the time being was keep Keith drilling and firing and load the rock out when cement grade was required. The number of men I had working the mine at this time was nine in total, one fitter, one electrician, three tractor men, three driller shotfirers, one man on the surface, the powder and crusherman.

The main production at this time was the north-west area of the South Anhydrite District, we were taking very good anhydrite out of this district. Unfortunately, a lot of it had gone out as cement rock in the past, instead of taking cement rock from the south-east area. If this had been done, the area would have been opened up by this time, ready to move into. Towards the end of January, we had a small single boom drill rig brought on trial, the Bison, which would certainly be a useful addition to the drilling side of the operation. Mounted on tracks, it was rather slow to move around but fast at boring the shot holes, plus it used a nine foot drill steel which would give us a much better pull when the drifts were fired. I would have this rig in the south-east area, we would have to put electric power cables in and a gate end box, just for starters, for the machine to run off. There would be some alterations to be made to it, air mist to damp the holes being one of them. I would leave Keith to drill with the Bison in the south-east area; I could see the place had possibilities, although one of the lads who had been at Newbiggin a long time expressed his doubts to me, and said we could not expect to go far before we hit faults and were stopped. This was a chance I would have to take, I thought, if we hit faults we would have to go through them or stop. It seemed to me little effort had been made in the past to go through a fault, work just came to a stop. Anyhow if we had to go through a fault, and we had to put steel girders in to keep the roof up, then that's what we would do. If not, then the mine would just have to close. Having said that, this particular mine had been closed at least twice before due to lack of orders, and the lads from here had come to Longriggs Mine for a short time.

The lads had their own system of working, I could see it worked well enough, and there would be no reason for me to make unnecessary changes. The lads on loading had two men hauling rock from the workings to the surface with the tractor trailer units, and one man on the GHH front end loader doing the loading. If we were short of a man, then the two lads on haulage would load their own tractors, this took a little longer on turn around time, and they would get slightly less tonnage. The lads on the drilling side had one man to do all the charging and shot firing, one man on the drill rig all the time, and one man to do either drilling or help out with the charging. At this time I would have Keith, who was the spare man, drilling full time in the south-east area. If the driller, Harold, should be off, or the charger shotfirer, then Keith would stand in on that job. If we were a little behind with the shotfiring, then I would have to put Keith in to help out on that job. All three shotfirers had to bar down before going to their jobs, it would be unsafe to have one man on his own to bar down. If the drillers were on top of their side of the job we would always have plenty of rock fired up to keep the loaders going. We always tried to have enough rock fired to keep the loaders going for at least two or three days, just in case of major breakdowns with the drill rigs. If we were short of men on the loading side, then I would have to put one of the shotfirers on haulage, as sometimes did happen. The lads worked well enough together, and had the good sense to know it was only the rock that we sent out of the mine, that kept us in business and jobs.

The demand for our rock had increased slightly at that time, with the prospect of even more being required, we were producing about eight hundred tons a week at that time, and sometimes a thousand. We had to have orders for at least that amount to keep the mine open. I had taken delivery of a new trailer that had been built for us, we would also be getting a new Ford County tractor to go with it, the trailer would be slightly larger than the ones in current use, and could carry two tons more than the other trailers. This would be a very useful addition to what we already had, but one of the older tractors would be taken from us for use at one of the other mines. Even so we would now have one tractor spare, we would always have a tractor serviced and ready in the event of one of the others breaking down, which they did quite frequently due to the hard life they had hauling rock. Since I had improved the roads by this time, although we still had plenty of work to carry out on the roads yet, it had made a difference to the breakdown frequency with the tractors, being much less bumpy for them when travelling loaded.

Perhaps now is as good a time as any to mention the wildlife around the mine, which was a treat to see. I had arrived at the mine late in the year and had taken little notice at that time, being I suppose, too busy. Christmas had come and passed now and we were coming in to spring. We had a horse in the field next to the office, it belonged to a farmer in the village and she looked forward to the lads coming out of the mine at the end of the shift, as they would give her pieces of cake they had saved from their bait, and she also liked mints one of the lads brought specially for her. As soon as she saw the lads coming up the hill, she would come over to the fence and wait for them. She seemed to have a foal every year, and this would always be a bonny little thing, but it would be a while before she would bring it close to us. By this time Arty had taken in a stray kitten. It had taken a lot of patience on his part to entice it into the small bait cabin he used on the surface. The mother had been feeding it on rabbits she had caught in the fields around, and an odd mouse or two. After a while the mother disap-peared, the kitten stayed around for quite a while after. The lads had been taking turns to bring cat food for it, and I think one of them took it home later on when it had become more tame. During the time I would spend at Newbiggin Mine, we would have one or two more kittens to look after, and they were always cared for by the lads.

We had a couple of wild ducks that came every year that I was there, they must have liked the little beck that ran through the place. Jackdaws nested inside the mine entrance, and I had been surprised by a family of

163

stoats that always seemed to be around, they were lovely to see, early on in the year. We also had a pair of lapwings that came every year, they were lovely to watch in flight, and gave the old crows some stick if they came onto their territory. Arty showed me where they had their eggs on top of a banking. Even the old crows were quite tame here and we all threw bits of bread for them, especially in the winter when they almost took the bread from my hand. They became so tame, in fact, as soon as they saw the lads coming up from the mine they gathered on each side of the road. As soon as their young could fly, they would bring them to the fence outside my office and sit making a racket until I gave them bread I had brought specially for them. We also had the occasional fox that came past first thing in the morning, and in the last year I would spend at Newbiggin Mine, one of the lads, Brian, and his friends would make a very interesting video of a vixen and her four cubs that had been born in one of our stock piles almost next to the mine entrance.

I had not realised until I had come to this mine just how much there was to be seen, if you took the trouble just to look. We had just about everything here, rabbits, partridge, pheasants, what a beautiful sight they were first thing in the morning. I had once joked to the lads that I would have to bring my shotgun, and they had replied to me, 'You can't shoot them, they are part of the family.' I had at one time been quite keen on shooting but I think it would be true to say I have never fired my gun since then, and have no intention of doing so again.

We had made a lot of progress at the mine by now, one thing that had pleased me the most being the fact that we now had the water under control. The roads had been improved, but we still had a lot to do yet, it was really one of those ongoing jobs that just had to be kept on top of. The new drill rig had proved itself and had been purchased at great expense, as had the new tractor and trailer. We had moved into the south-east area and had two or three good drifts of Anpak quality rock to go at, and plenty of cement quality. All I could do now was to hope we did not hit the faults the geologist had told us we should hit—two bad ones I had been told lay in front of the heading we were now taking north by east. I had been around to have a good look in the old workings to see just where the faults were running; they were there to see and it looked very much like we would soon hit one of them. I would have to make sure the roofs had plenty of rock left in them, eighteen inches would be fine. We had good drifts in this area, they were of good height at around twelve feet, and we were getting into better rock with every shot fired. I could see the difference in the anhydrite quite plainly. Yes, it was definitely getting better. I had sent some poorer quality out when we had first started in this area, but that would be a thing of the past from now on.

The roofs were always on my mind, I spent a lot of my time checking them out on my rounds of the mine, we put roof bolts in if we had any doubt at all. If the roof should be poked then we would have to mesh and bolt, any we had that may need to be bolted would have to have a No Road board up until we could bolt it up. At this time we were working most weekends, and sometimes had to work on to five in the evening but it was nice to have orders for our rock, the quarry being in full swing at this time sending good gypsum over to the works to be put on the stock pile for making board. At the same time they put a lot of the cement grade rock onto our stock pile. Things were beginning to look up, the manager told me we were to get a brand new loader, a Toro front end loader. The lads did not believe me when I told them, but when I said two of the lads, and Cyril the fitter, were to get a trip down to Cornwall to see one in action in a tin mine, they still did not believe it. They had reacted just the same when I had told them we would be taking delivery of a new tractor trailer unit and drill rig. I think it would be fair to say, poor old Newbiggin Mine had been running on a shoestring for years, and had always been treated as the poor relative compared to the other mines at Kirkby Thore.

I had approached the mines engineer at this time, and asked if it would be possible to get a new rising main put in on the north side, which would do away with the pipeline now in use. The pipeline had been nothing more than a nuisance to me ever since I had been at the mine; it had to come all the way from the 50 h.p. pump on the north side, a distance of some seven hundred yards or more through the old workings, to the rising main near the entrance. It seemed to me that every day I would have repairs of one kind or another to make to that pipeline, the pressure on it when the pump started up was enormous, due to its length. The pipes would kick all over the place on start up, the joints would leak and where the pipes had become corroded, they soon developed splits due to the great pressure on them, causing more flooding. By putting a new rising main down from the small

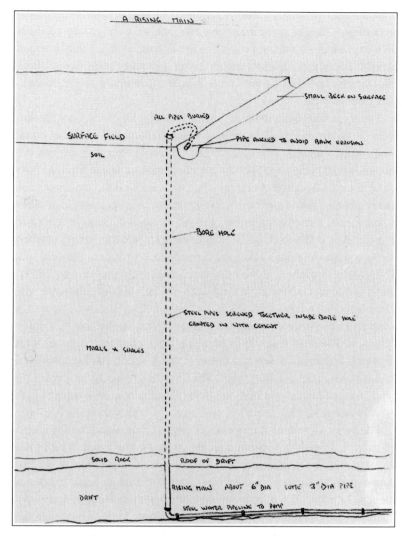

beck on the surface, we could reduce the length of the pipeline to only two hundred yards, from the pump to the new rising main. This had to be an advantage to us, and I was very relieved when the manager arranged for the new rising main to be put in.

The surveyors, a really good bunch of lads, duly arrived to measure up;

the outside boring gang arrived and made a start on boring the hole down to the old workings, from the surface. It did not take very long for the job to be completed. I was impressed with the accuracy when the drill bit came through the roof in the old workings, in two words, spot on. The pipes from the new rising main to the well that were not now required could be dismantled and removed, some we kept for spares ourselves, some being taken away for use in the Longriggs Mine.

At this time, we were still being hit throughout the company with redundancies, pressure from competition in the plaster and board markets being great, and the need to reduce cost at all levels in the company. Shortly after the rising main had been completed, the outside boring gang were made redundant, our rising main had been their last job. The pressure on all of us in management to reduce cost wherever possible never ceased, and it seemed that redundancy throughout the company now seemed to be the norm, every plant and mine had been hit from managers down. The lads had been given a new deal, agreed between company and unions: they would have to be more flexible in working practices, meaning more work with fewer men wherever possible, efficiency being of the utmost importance—in fact the overall reduction in the company workforce had been set at around 15%, or something like about three in every twenty. Those who wished could volunteer for redundancy, the deal in itself being attractive to those who wanted to take advantage of it, and many at Kirkby Thore did.

A new mine had been opened at Barrow-on-Soar near Nottingham, and this would eventually have a plaster mill that would have the largest output of any plant of its type in Europe. I thought back over the past few years and realised how lucky I had been myself. I had survived a number of redundancies at Kirkby Thore up to now and had seen many of my old workmates go, voluntarily or otherwise. Almost all of the older end had gone by now, and a great many of the younger end, and morale was at its lowest.

In the meantime, those of us left could do no more than just get on with it, which is what we did, among much speculation as to what if anything would happen in a few years' time from now. There had been plans to open a new quarry when the one at Houtsay closed, planning permission had been sought and granted for this quarry that would be over on the Long Marton side. The surface would be taken off to get at the old Stamphill workings, and rock taken out by opencast methods. It was hoped some of the miners who would be made redundant would find employment there. Plans for the quarry have been put on ice for the time being at least. We all knew time was running out for our mines, trials had already been carried out using a synthetic type gypsum obtained from the power plants. It looked to us very likely that the nineties would see the end of gypsum mining in the Eden valley. We would be the very last of the miners in this valley, there would be no more after we were gone, the old man, the lead and barytes miners, had gone before us, we had lasted well over one hundred years.

Things at the mine had by now improved, we had opened up the south-east area well and truly; we had our good days and our bad days, break-downs when we could have done without them, but in general things were not too bad. We had moved into the nineties nice and quietly, we could load out the best of anhydrite at 92%, and the best of cement quality rock as and when it was wanted. We had a good run on orders, so good in fact that for a short while two shifts had to be put in. But like all good things, that soon came to an end and we were back to regular days again.

All the mine's foremen had from April '89 been made, under a new deal agreement, supervisors. Up to now we had always had two under-managers in the mines, the two young men who had held those positions had decided to leave mining, one to take up a position out of mining, and the other to move into management in the works. It would seem to us they were making a wise move the way things were shaping up. We still had our orders for rock, although they did appear to fluctuate quite a lot. At our monthly team briefing with the mine's manager, we were constantly being asked to make cost reductions wherever possible, and being told about what the competition were or were not doing. I think the lads were sick and tired of hearing the same old thing month after month. One of the reasons we had lost some of our orders for Anpak was the closure of many of the coal mines that had used it up to now. At almost every team brief now there would be a list of redundancies throughout the company, so many from this mine, so many from that works, it seemed to be never ending. What a pity really, just when poor old Newbiggin Mine had got back onto its feet. It had taken us a year or two to make it into a good little mine, the lads had worked very hard at it over the last four years. We had made many improvements in that time: the water had been brought under control, it was no longer a nuisance to us; we had made ourselves really good roads; we had opened up the south-east area and mined through the faults we were to hit, and found top quality anhydrite.

The old north-west area had long since been abandoned. The ventilation had been improved tremendously when we had driven two new roads through from the south-east area workings into the old north-east workings, cutting our running times to and from the surface crusher. It would be true to say, the new drill rig cost a lot more to run than the old Holrigs, simply because it ran off electricity, and the Holrigs were air driven, requiring little maintenance compared to the Bison rig. The tonnage coming out of a drift fired with the Bison drill rig, about 80 tons per firing, would be far more than that fired with the Holrig, but repairs were much more expensive for the Bison, compared to the Holrig. One thing the Bison rig did have fitted, and that was a solid steel canopy over the operator of the machine, and the front end loaders also had a steel canopy fitted to them to protect the drivers from injury should a roof fall occur. We had learned from experience in the past, if a roof did deteriorate, as they did in the old workings, the sheer vibration and noise of the machine working could cause pieces to come off, if conditions were right. The type of rock we were mining became very damp during hot weather in the summer months and suffered from condensation. Any small cracks in the roof had to be looked at very carefully, small flakes would be dropping off the roof all the time, although they were mostly too small to cause anyone harm. We did however have to watch out for any sag in the roof. If this occurred, it would just have to be fired off and bolted and if marl were exposed it would also have to be meshed.

I have tried on occasions on the old north side during my rounds to check the pumps on that side, to bar off slabs of sagging roof that I might find, up to six inches thick. Roof that had come away due to condensation and air entering through cracks over the years would look solid but a week later I would find that piece had just dropped out. It was just as well almost all the drifts off the main road were closed off in those old workings; some of the piles of roofing that had come away were six foot or more deep and many tons in weight.

Houtsay Quarry had closed down, having been worked out by the contractor, and had been filled in and landscaped over and a good job had been done over there; it was difficult to see where it had been when completed.

All the mines at Kirkby Thore were now feeling the pinch. Longriggs Mine had been put onto one shift due to a reduction in the overall tonnage being required by the plant; Birks Mine had now gone onto two shifts; many of the lads from all three mines had opted to take their redundancy having decided to get out. It seemed hard to believe just how quickly things had changed, due to the recession, throughout the country, especially in the building industry, which of course hit us hard. We had hoped only a short time before that there would be an upturn and things would improve. In fact, things had looked quite good for a short while for us at Newbiggin Mine, orders for our rock had picked up and were looking good. It had seemed strange to us that no new under-managers had been brought in, but I suppose in the present difficulties it was understandable with the mines running down slowly but surely.

From September '90 the mine's Supervisors were to be given an enhanced status, the company had decided to revise its works supervisory structure. I would now have the grand title of Mine Superintendent. I rather liked that, perhaps I could have a bigger hat to go with the title, any increase in salary would of course be based on performance, this would be assessed annually by the mine's manager. One thing I had learned years ago whilst shop steward was how easy it is to do an awful amount of work using only a pencil and a sheet of paper. It seemed at the time we had more paperwork to do than anything else, and we seemed to get more and more. We did our best to look on the bright side, but I found it more and more difficult to keep up the morale of the lads. It was very understandable too, especially the younger lads who were only naturally worried about their jobs; they had small children and mortgages to think about.

By this time, the crows around the mine had got to know me a little too well. I had one brave enough to come into my office and wait until I gave it a piece of cake, while the rest would line up on the fencing posts and wait in hope for a tit bit, which they knew would be given. I could now walk up to them and feed them by hand, even the cheeky jackdaws were in on the act, along with the odd pigeon and numerous small birds. I had plenty to think about as Superintendent at Newbiggin Mine, there would always be an inspection of one sort or another, but I like to think we were always well on top of any inspections we were to have, and I can honestly say I can't remember having a bad report, usually they were complimentary. But this was only because the lads made the effort, and took a pride in their mine. They were just as keen as I was that the mine should be efficient in so far as we could make it so, both in keeping our costs to a minimum and in the quality of the rock we produced and the amount produced. We all had the good sense to know our jobs were at stake. At this time with the orders for rock dropping, we had to work maintenance on more than just one day a week, sometimes we only worked two production shifts in the week, this gave us ample opportunity to get all those little jobs completed that needed to be done.

To us in the mines, it looked very much like we were melting away slowly like the snow in a thaw, as one great poet once wrote. Over the past eighteen months or so I had some lads leave, and lads from other mines brought in as replacements. I now had two fitters, which had made a big difference to the running of the mine from my point of view, being able to keep on top of the maintenance side of the job. It had been hard work for Cyril when he had been on his own at the mine, especially with the heavier type of work lifting steel plates about on the crusher at times, and changing the wheels on the vehicles in the mine, although all the lads helped out as and when they could. One thing that had made life better for the lad on the crusher had been the water spray I had fixed on the hopper to kill off the dust, shortly after I had come to Newbiggin Mine, and the new steel plates and pans for the drag link, that had been put in later on. The belt from the crusher to the top of the bin had also been renewed, and this had stopped a lot of dust dropping onto the pans as the rock travelled up the belt. The jackdaws and the occasional pigeon would begin building their nests on the pans, and we had to discourage them from doing this. In the past we had allowed them to build a nest or two on the pans, and try to rear their young in there. They would be snug enough, because the pans were covered in, although the noise was unbearable, but their young always seemed to get caught up in the belt sooner or later, so I had the twigs and sheep wool removed as soon as they appeared.

Since I had been at Newbiggin Mine, we had always had a party of students arrive in June. They were all from the department of mining at Newcastle University, and had been coming to Newbiggin Mine for many years. They had always been used to Joe giving them the run of the office and the empty back room adjacent to the office, which would be filled to capacity with their equipment. They would survey the countryside around the mine and finish off with a day or two in the old workings on the north side. I think they were with us for about ten days in all, staying in digs locally. They were in the capable hands of Norman and his assistant, Rob, and were always a pleasant bunch of youngsters, full of the joys of life, livening the old place up for the time they were with us. When they arrived at the mine, naturally they piled into the office and began to bring in their equipment. I being new at that time and this being the first time I had met them, thought this to be an invasion of my privacy, and gave them a right good bulling, as we say in Cumbria. When we were to get to know each other better we became good friends, and I looked forward to having them at the mine.

I think it was in June '90 the students arrived as usual, but I could see all was not well really. Later on in the week Rob told me this would be the very last time they would be coming to the mine, the department would be transferred from Newcastle University to Leeds University. I asked why this should be, and he told me it was because so few students were interested in mining these days the department would have to close down. I could see why—when so many mines were closing down in this country, what would be the point? Almost all of those youngsters at the mine this time would be taking up jobs in another country. What a waste. We shook hands for the last time. Rob did not know at that time what his future would be, Norman would be retiring. I could only say goodbye and wish them luck for the future, as they did for me.

I had time to think back over the years about how things had changed as they inevitably do. When I had first started at the mines there had been four working mines in all at Kirkby Thore, now there were three, and where there had been three shifts on at Birks Head Mine, now only two, and where Longriggs Mine had two, now just the one. At this time, even the one shift at Newbiggin Mine did not look too safe, we were hardly sending any tonnage out at all. When I had accepted the job as foreman at Newbiggin Mine I had been but one of six mine shift foremen, now I was but one of four. One sadly had died, and one had taken redundancy. There were no under-managers now, shortly before we had two; of the four foremen who had retired when I and three others had been made up to foremen, two sadly had died.

A mine is very much the same as a living thing, it starts off in a small way with perhaps a couple of drifts, it develops from them to something bigger, with many more drifts, and grows bigger as time passes by. Vibrating with life and activity, it gives of its best, like a flower in full bloom, and then when it is finally exhausted it slowly dies off, and is abandoned, the life that had been within it gone forever. I had often tried to imagine what it had been like many years before, when I had spent so much of my time exploring the old mines in Scordale near Hilton. How many men had there been working there, what it must have been like in those mines, the sounds of the hammer as it hit the steel the man would be boring the shot hole with, what kind of light they would have had to work with, having no more than a candle stuck in a ball of clay on the side of the drift. While exploring these old mines I had sometimes switched off the electric light I had been using, and lit one of the candles I had always carried with me for emergencies, just to see what it was like. I don't think it could have been very good for a man's eyesight. When I arrived home after one of my trips, I would think about those old workings I had explored, how dark and quiet they had been all those years until I had entered into them, and disturbed them with my presence. But at least I had been privileged enough to have seen them the old Wilson level in the Dowscar mine, the sheer craftsmanship of the stone arched drift in the lower pony level with the trap doors to drop rock into the tubs, stonework like that would still be there years from now.

I had read many books on the old lead mines of this area, and had always intended to put pen to paper myself and leave some small record behind of the gypsum mines. Perhaps one day when these mines are no more than just a memory, like those old mines in Scordale, someone will be interested enough to want to know a little about them and how they were worked.

By this time the mine's blacksmith had taken his redundancy, and would not be replaced. To us this really was a bad omen, mines without a blacksmith, a bit like running an engine with no oil. We in the meantime could do no more than as before, get on with it. We seemed to be having more days on maintenance than production at this time; '91 had not been a particularly good year as far as we in the mines were concerned, with the severe recession in the UK building industry, and three years of fierce competition. The restructuring within the company had brought many more redundancies than even we had anticipated. It was almost Christmas again, what would '92 have in store for us, we wondered, as we all went off for our Christmas holiday, along with those who had taken their redundancy at that time. The one good thing that had come out of the new deal previously had been the Saturday and Sunday off that we now enjoyed, at least we could now plan our weekends off better.

I think I can safely say the mines at this time were more efficient than they had ever been, enormous savings had been made as everyone tried to save on expenditure wherever possible, and try to be as cost efficient as possible. We at Newbiggin Mine now worked four shifts on production, and one on maintenance normally; if our orders were down, then we might work only two shifts on production and three on maintenance. To keep the mine open we had to have orders for around eight hundred to one thousand tons a week, and at this time we were nowhere near this figure. But we had hopes—a company producing fertiliser had shown an interest in our rock, it would be used as a coating on their fertiliser product, after it had been ground to a fine powder. It was hoped we might have an order for some four hundred tons a week, or there about. We had already sent a container load for testing some time before, although we had to alter the setting on our crusher for that order, as the rock had to be crushed down to around half an inch. We had some slight problems with some larger pieces of rock getting through, but this could be put to rights using screens.

It was May, and the smell of the hawthorn as I walked along the road to the mine entrance first thing in the mornings really was beautiful. The weather had now taken up and made us all feel a lot better, despite the threat of redundancies. At this time I had noticed how the general morale of the lads had dropped in all the mines at Kirkby Thore; at one time they would always be having a laugh and a bit of fun, but now hardly a smile. It had been tough enough years ago at times, and we had gone through some hard times then, wondering if the job would last, and the first redundancies had come as a blow to us, but each time it seemed to me we had always come back again stronger than before. This time, however, I really had doubts in my mind, and I could understand how the younger lads were feeling just now. There seemed to be no way I could reassure them, even though this mine was running well, and had plenty of good anhydrite and cement quality rock left in it to be taken out. I knew also that if orders could be increased, and a system of belts put in along with a face crusher, the tonnage could be obtained easily with fewer men than we had at this time. All we could do was hope the orders for the fertiliser company would not be lost but hopefully increase and keep us in business for some time to come.

We had plenty of rock fired in the drifts in the mine, and were well on top of any maintenance work that had to be done. We had plenty of time on maintenance just now, but we always seemed to have plenty to do anyhow, so it worked out well for us. The height of the roof in the main haulage road had been found to be too low, and to keep within the regulation we had to set about getting it right. The reason for the roof being too low in certain parts, had been our past efforts at making the road better for the tractors running up and down it in the first place, when we had used hundreds of tons of Anpak dust to fill and level off with over the years. We had to scrape quite a bit off the road at three places to be within the regulation height, but a good job was done and the road would be even better by the time we had completed the job. The water in the mine at this time gave us no problems at all, being well and truly under control, the mine ventilation was good, we had been using only one fan for some time now, thus cutting our electricity bill, and this had proved sufficient for the purpose. I was ready now to build some stoppings in the workings to keep the ventilation good in there, and had already decided where they were to be built, leaving an air door in place at eleven cross cut for the tractors to come through when leading rock from the cement drifts in the top side of the workings. The faults we had expected to give us problems in the workings had not caused us any problems so far, and the anhydrite we had just now would be of the best quality; if nothing else was looking good just now, at leat this mine was.

As June came around, I must say I really missed the young students, and I half expected to bump into them as I did my rounds on the old north side, where they finished off their week at the mine; the only reminder of them being some of their names on the side of the drifts. The weather at this time of the year really was lovely, we were into July and I would celebrate my birthday. Things were going well, the only thing to spoil it had been a further fifty-eight redundancies at another of the company works, Gotham. this had come as a blow to us, we had not expected it would be so many, but we could do nothing about it, only wait and see where the next lot would be. In the meantime, I had decided to take my dear wife out for a meal to forget about all the doom and gloom around. We arrived at the pub in the village of Sandford, only a couple of miles away from Warcop, at about seven fifteen. We had our meal and enjoyed it, my wife had just decided what she would have for a sweet—I unfortunately would not be wanting any as I had slumped over having suffered a stroke. I came around in the ambulance on the way to hospital, my mining days were over for good. I would be officially retired from the end of November '92.

Newbiggin Mine closed at the end of November '92, four of the lads took their redundancy, the four that were now left were moved to Longriggs Mine, along with the electrician. The fertiliser company have since placed an order for Anpak and the lads who were sent to Longriggs Mine go back to Newbiggin Mine to produce this rock as and when they are required to do so. Hopefully they may continue to do so for some time to come for their sake. Even as I now write, in April '93, I read with interest an article in my local newspaper:

Rail v. road debate over plan for new Kirkby Thore plant.

British Gypsum want to build a new plant, to process up to one million tonnes per annum of desulphogypsum, a by-product from the Drax power station in North Yorkshire, this could result in an extra 55 lorries travelling through that village each day. The local planning officer will be recommending the councillors support the plan in principle, but be minded to grant approval only if rail transport be used. The works manager said, while the proposal would not bring new jobs it would help to secure existing jobs at Kirkby Thore, which has been hit by redundancies in recent years.

I can understand why there have been objectors to the increase in heavy lorries coming through the village by the usual Friends of the Lakes, friends of something else, etc., etc., and I must say, in my opinion, the rail option would no doubt be the better and more sensible one. The company have already stated rail transport would be the preferred option, but without the availability of grants it would be excessively expensive. I can only say I look forward to the outcome of the proposal with interest, and as for those who so strenuously object to local people being kept in some form of employment other than catering purely for the tourists who come to our beautiful valley each year, it's jobs such as those provided at Kirkby Thore for local people that stop the whole valley becoming no more than just a giant sized holiday camp, with holiday cottages for those who can afford to buy them up.

Just when I thought I had completed this book I found I had a little more to add to it. I saw a notice in my local newspaper:

> To all Birks Head Miners, both past and present, a Wake will be held at Long Marton pub, for Birks Head Mine. 30 July 1993. all those who wish to attend be there 2.30 p.m.

I had to be there, even though it had been many years since I had worked in that mine, as far back as 1971. I arrived at the pub around 2.40p.m. I saw a No Road Charged Shots board at the entrance to the pub, and for some unknown reason I stopped automatically for a moment; then, realising it had been placed there in good humour by one of the lads, I entered. There were faces there I recognised instantly, and some I could only remember vaguely. As I have mentioned earlier in this book, the names of some were the same, but the faces were different—sons of men I had worked with many years before, having followed their fathers into mining. I sat down with one of my old workmates, Dabber, and we had a good crack about some of the things we had got up to all those years ago, and a good laugh at some of them. I could spend no more than an hour in their company, although I would dearly have liked to have spent a few more.

I was told Birks Head Mine had closed from 30 July 1993. The mighty Birks closed down—it didn't seem possible! We had always looked upon this mine as the one most likely to survive of all the mines at Kirkby Thore. Some of the lads had been transferred to jobs at the works, some had taken redundancy. I was told all the mines superintendents who were there after I had retired had now been made redundant, or would be from the end of August '93. It seemed to me this would be the end of gypsum mining at Kirkby Thore after one hundred and thirteen years—the end of mining in the Eden Valley, and those of us still alive could claim to be the last of the miners in the Eden Valley. Unlike the early lead and barytes miners, nothing so far has been written about us, until now.

At this moment in time Longriggs Mine is still open, although we were told by the mines manager at the end of 1991 that Longriggs Mine would be closing down in September of '93. I know that as I am writing now, little old Newbiggin Mine is still producing anhydrite, as and when required, sometimes three to four days a week, and it does give me some satisfaction to know it is still in operation.

To Be a Gypsum Miner

HOW ITS ALL ENDING UP

WHAT THE LATEST CONTINUOUS MINER LOOKS LIKE OPERATING IN A GYPSUM MINE FROM PHOTOGRAPH

COST £1·5M   ABOUT 24' LONG

Stamphill Mine Well Drift
1968–69

Drilling

Hand machines

Loading

Hough 30
Vibrator to side belts, to main conveyor system, to underground bunker, from bunker to bins and crusher on surface via main conveyor system. From bins on surface, to works, via overland aerial ropeway in skips.

Other vehicles

Ford 2000 tractor with trailer for powder.
Hudson scaling vehicle.
Haulage way still used to bring materials into mine, from surface to Well Drift west area. Also from surface to Birks Mine, old north area, via the nine belt connecting drift.
All the vehicles used in the mine were stripped down on the surface and brought into the mine, then rebuilt by the fitters.

Birks Head Mine 1969–71

Drilling

Hand machines. Chaside drill rig.

Loading

Hough 30. Hough 50. Drott.
Vibrator to side belts, to main conveyor system, via nine belt connecting

drift to Stamphill Mine underground bunkers, from bunker to bins and crusher on surface at Stamphill Mine. To works via overland aerial ropeway in skips.

Other vehicles

Ford 2000 tractor powder, fitter's tractor, old Bedford TK converted by the fitters, with boom and cage for roof scaling and charging purposes. This vehicle had stabilisers to set vehicle level before lifting boom, *the first* in the Kirkby Thore mines. Haulage system still in use: tubs, at this time, to bring materials from surface mine entrance, on the Long Marton side, into the mine from surface to bait cabin at bottom of hill. Chaside drill rig and front end loaders had been brought into Birks Head Mine, this way, stripped down on the surface and brought into the mine on bogeys, rebuilt by fitters.

Area covered 1992 one square mile approx.

Longriggs Mine 1972–87

Drilling

Secoma drill rigs 2. for main drilling.
Atlas Copco drill rig 1. Short period (not known).
Road header cutting machine (trial period one month).

Loading

Hough 50—used to load tractor trailer units at face.
Terex—used to load tractor trailer units at face. Vibrator used for short time on rope belt, and later on north-west side after conveyor system put in. After conveyor system put in Volvo dumpers, and Muir Hill tractor trailer units not used, GHH Scooptram came in, later the Toro Scooptram, both to load into face crusher, in workings. Rock via conveyor system to underground main crusher, to works, via conveyor system.

Haulage vehicles.

Muir Hill tractor trailer units, used to haul rock from crusher to surface before underground bunker completed.

Volvo dump trucks. Muir Hill tractor trailer units
used to haul rock from face to crusher. After bunker completed crusher to
bunker to works via main haulage belt, put in same time as bunker system.

Other vehicles

Hudson scaler 2.
Chaside scaler and charging vehicle 1.
Normet scaling and charging vehicle 1.
Ford tractors fitters and powder.
Inter mines Landrovers.
Ford County. Powder tractor (later).

Area covered 1992—1.75 miles x 0.75 miles approx.

Newbiggin Mine 1987–93

Drilling

Holrig drill rigs 2.
Bison drill rig 1.

Loading

GHH Scooptram 2. Later, Toro Scooptram, 1.

Haulage

Ford County tractor trailer units 3.
From workings to surface crusher, to storage bins, to works via road,
haulage contractor.

Others

GHH. Converted to scaler.
Ford 2000–5000 tractors 3. Mine use, and powder.

Area covered 1992—1 mile x 1,000 yds. approx.

Postscript

Of the 200 or more men working at the mines in 1968, there are only 17 at Kirkby Thore today.